VALLEY OF TINY SHADOWS

Valley of Tiny Shadows

Bedside Tales of Critically Ill Newborns

Linda M. Sacks, M.D.

Gamzu
Savannah
2012

Published in the United States of America by
Gamzu, LLC
406 Wheeler Street
Savannah, Georgia 31401

Library of Congress Control Number: 2011942061

ISBN 978-0-9847558-0-6 (hardcover)
ISBN 978-0-9847558-1-3 (softcover)

Manufactured in the United States of America

From
Nana Lin
to
Daniel and Alexandra

Contents

Preface   ix
Acknowledgments   xvii

1. A Time to Live and a Time to Die   3
2. Jonathan's Miracle   19
3. Motorcycle Boy   33
4. The Long Night   47
5. The Cowards We Are   60
6. Unexpected Disaster   84
7. Elijah   106
8. Be Careful What You Wish For   120
9. A Tale of Two Trisomies: Stephan   139
10. A Tale of Two Trisomies: Taylor Marie   157
11. Rooming in to Die   174

Glossary   195

PREFACE

This book is a semiautobiographical, nonfiction work about critically ill and dying newborns. I am a *neonatologist*, a physician who specializes in the care of such infants. This project was conceived one night in March 2001 during a dinner conversation with my neonatal colleagues and our practice administrators. Although the meeting was set up as a forum for the airing of business concerns at a time of transition, our conversation had wandered to a discussion of good vacation spots and retirement plans. One of the group asked me, as the senior (that is, oldest!) neonatologist, "How much longer do you think you'll practice, Linda? And what will you do with the rest of your life?"

I answered that I didn't want to retire any time soon, but that in retirement, perhaps I'd write a book about dying infants who were successfully brought back to life, those that didn't make it, and the ethical issues involved in each case. I actually had one example in mind (see Chapter 2), and told Jonathan's story. My colleagues showed enthusiastic interest, some even sharing their own heart-wrenching stories. I'm still not retired, and I still continue to enjoy my work with sick babies and their families. Nevertheless, I've decided to put some of the meaningful stories, the ones that live uninvited in my subconscious, to paper.

As I wrote, the incredible changes in medical technology that have occurred between the mid 1970's, during my internship, and now, the first decade of the twenty-first century, jumped out at me from the typewritten page. I pondered the equally profound changes in ethics that have found their way into medicine over the last thirty years. I realized how the age-old potential for newborn suffering and the medical profession's newly discovered respect for parental participation and general principles of autonomy have affected the way we now practice critical care in the setting of a hospital neonatal intensive care unit *(NICU)*.

During that thirty-year span, the neonatal mortality rate has fallen by fifty percent in the United States, with the greatest decline occurring among *VLBW* (*very low birth weight infants*), those weighing less than 1.5 *kilograms* at birth (just over three pounds five ounces).[1] During the past three decades the attitude of the pediatric and nonmedical community toward neonatal death, and the spoken and unspoken decisions surrounding its occurrence have also changed markedly. For example, during my neonatal fellowship training in the mid-1970's, parents were never asked if support for their sick and extremely premature infants should be initiated. No one solicited a worried mother's or grieving father's opinion on continuation, limitation, or withdrawal of heroic therapy.[2] By centuries of tradition, medicine was autocratic and paternalistic. Doctors in charge made decisions on behalf of children in their care. Sometimes these physicians were only residents in training.

As medical ethics gained acceptance as a specialty, was gradually integrated into all branches of medicine, and became a part of every practice and in some larger hospitals even established as a free-standing department, those old autocratic and paternalistic attitudes rotated almost 180 degrees. Today, patient autonomy, or in the case of infants, surrogate autonomy by the parents, is the rule. Doctors rarely initiate life support without discussions with parents, and only after obtaining their informed acquiescence. Conversely, doctors rarely limit or discontinue medical support, without full disclosure to and consent from families. Final decision-making authority rests clearly in parental hands. The legal, ethical, and medical assumption is that parents are capable of decisions to initiate, pursue, limit, or stop medical therapy based upon their perception of their babies' best interests. Sometimes this assumption works out well for all concerned. Unfortunately, at other times, families and physicians cannot agree on the best course for the infant. The babies, of course, have no say in this decision making. In addition, the negative or positive outcome for the infants, and whether the decisions that were made turned out to be in their best interests, is always subjective. *Handicap* is a relative term.

Neonatal research has produced science fiction–like advances in supportive and lifesaving care, most notably *surfactant* for treatment of *hyaline membrane disease, extracorporeal membrane oxygenation (ECMO,* or heart lung bypass) for respiratory failure, *inhaled nitric oxide therapy (iNO)* for *pulmonary hypertension (PPHN),* and increased ability to deliver safe and effective *total parenteral (intravenous) nutrition (TPN).* Monitoring technology, ventilators, and surgical techniques have also progressed at an incredible pace. Working in our current critical care medical milieu, one could easily get the feeling that death results only when we run out of technology to keep a heart beating. As physicians facing hopeless situations, we often question whether it would be better to think in terms of what more *should* be done for the patient, rather than what more *can* be done. Must we always use every drug, piece of equipment, or high tech procedure to which we have access? At what cost to society? At what price in terms of human suffering?

In 2006 the American Academy of Pediatrics (AAP) and the American Heart Association (AHA) took a bold step when those professional societies recommended through the Neonatal Resuscitation Program (NRP) that infants less than twenty-three weeks gestation, babies with *Trisomy 13* and *Trisomy 18,* and infants with *anencephaly* be considered nonviable.[3] Accordingly, the AAP and AHA advised that medical heroics be withheld in the delivery room, and that only comfort care be offered to these unfortunate babies. Committing this statement to writing represents a paradigm shift in thinking about neonatal resuscitation. Care in those delineated circumstances is considered futile, and not of benefit to the infant patient.[4]

Obstetricians and pediatricians are strongly advised, time permitting, to discuss such situations with the involved families in advance of delivery, advising them that no medical treatment other than comfort care should be given. Having an authoritative text backing up this kind of medical advice to families makes presenting comfort care as an alternative to invasive therapy an easier task. In some cases, however, it sets up an excruciating conflict between families and physicians. Some of those situations are included in this book. By relating my own gut-wrenching and soul-searching experiences, I hope to give the reader a personal perspective on these changes in decision making that often leave physicians frustrated, angry, and feeling very helpless in the face of parental involvement in a medical arena in which emotions on both sides can become obstacles to babies' best interests. I hope that the reader will be able to glimpse the thought processes of physicians as they deal on a daily basis with the ever-changing advances in science, the increasingly complex technology, family dynamics, infants' physiologic reactions, and clinical triumphs and failures that are all part of neonatology of the past and of today.

In writing this book, medical accuracy was of vital importance to me. Many books about high-risk infants, written by parents, are filled with medical naivety and inaccuracies, frequently maximizing a tale of medical triumphs and minimizing the toll of medical suffering. To be fair and thorough, I have also looked to the published literature of the last three decades to assess the views of my neonatal colleagues and to bring the opinions of medical ethicists to the reader, regarding parental, societal, and medical and nursing staff reactions to neonatal death or to the anticipation of such death. I have woven this background material throughout the writing. I hope my own growth as a caring doctor is reflected as well.

In the last three decades I have witnessed or have been in charge at many neonatal deaths and near-deaths. Some of these scenarios involving the critically ill neonate were decidedly different or more poignant than others. Some left an impression on me that colored the remainder of my career or changed my professional behavior. I've chosen these few cases as the basis of this most personal treatise. Although it was not my explicit intention, the reader will find the historical development of neonatology as a specialty embedded in the chronological tale of these death and near-death experiences. I discovered that only through this historical perspective can the reader understand the actions and emotions of the parents, doctors, and nurses. I hope that through these cases, neonatal medicine's history will come alive for the reader.

The book is divided into two parts. The first part contains, in chronological order, poignant stories about critically ill newborns, rich with emotion and medical history, most with unhappy endings. Many of the stories have central cores involving neonatal ethics. The second part is a glossary of medical terms, which are italicized in the text the first time they appear in each chapter.

I have included many medical details that I believe add critical background material for each story, but I have tried to keep my explanations accessible to nonmedical readers. Where there was too much information to include in the body of the chapter, I included endnotes and/or an explanation in the glossary. The nonmedical reader can skip the detailed explanations in the endnotes or glossary; the medical aspects of the stories required for understanding what happened will still make sense. I hope, however, that general readers with a sense of curiosity about what goes on behind the NICU doors will enhance their scientific knowledge by referring to the endnotes and glossary. I believe that this volume will also provide a useful and user-friendly introduction to neonatology for students in medicine, nursing, respiratory therapy, and pharmacy; residents in obstetrics and pediatrics; and any other professionals who may rotate through neonatology or obstetrics such as case managers, discharge planners, surgeons, pediatric subspecialty consultants, and social workers.

The stories in this volume are all basically true. Other than my own name, I've changed the names of physicians, nurses, and hospitals. I refer to babies by fictitious first names. I represented family names by randomly selected first letters. I have changed some nonmedical details in order to protect privacy. Names and places of historical and scientific interest have been retained. When I couldn't recall the exact words of conversations, I took narrow license with what had been said to get at the crux of the conversation that I've related to the reader. At times I interviewed physician and nursing staff who were involved in the patient's care, and I spoke directly with two families, five years and twenty years respectively after the birth of their children. Each of the families in this book taught me an important life-lesson by allowing me to be involved in the intimate circumstances of their child's care, and for that I remain eternally grateful.

I hope you will find as much meaning in the stories that I've committed to these pages as I did in my professional participation in them as they unfolded. I hope that those who read this volume will gain a better understanding of the triumphs, failures, and most of all, the conflicts that arise in the care of the most vulnerable members of our society. I welcome feedback, and I invite readers to share thoughts with me by snail mail or e-mail. I will do my best to respond personally, or to put reader comments (with initials, not names) in a future volume.

Linda M. Sacks, M.D.
May 2011

1. The United States' infant mortality rate only ranks about 30th–46th in the world, depending on the year at which one looks and the countries included. We are always worse than Cuba, Poland, and French Polynesia. This ranking, however, is somewhat misleading. Some states in the United States count every live birth in the denominator, even late miscarriages at twenty weeks, with weights under four hundred grams. If the miscarried fetus has a heart rate, it is counted as a live birth. Most other countries have stricter interpretations of live birth. Certain European states and Japan only count as live births cases where an infant breathes at birth, which makes their reported infant mortality rates somewhat lower. In addition, the United States has an astounding rate of prematurity, nearly twelve percent. Most infant deaths occur in this group of smaller infants. However, if one compares the death rate for any given birth weight or gestational age, U.S.A. babies do as well or better than those in many countries who rank overall ahead of us. The public health issue for the United States is the high rate of prematurity and the postnatal death rate through accidents.

2. See Robert Stinson and Peggy Stinson, *Long Dying of Baby Andrew* (Boston: Little, Brown and Co., 1979).

3. American Heart Association and American Academy of Pediatrics, *Textbook of Neonatal Resuscitation*, 5th ed. (2006).

4. But even that may be changing. A recent article ("An Infant With Trisomy 18 and a Ventricular Septal Defect," *Pediatrics* 127 [2011], 754, by A. Janvier et al.) reports a child with Trisomy 18 who underwent repair of a VSD. Pandora's box has been opened.

ACKNOWLEDGMENTS

During the three-year course of writing this book, there were many individuals who encouraged me, read multiple drafts of *Valley of Tiny Shadows*, and provided me with story details that I had forgotten or even not been aware of. Alex Sweeney and Lydia Harris, neonatal nurse practitioners, provided encouragement and information. I appreciate the insight of Mary Sue Arthur, also a neonatal nurse practitioner. Her helpful criticism of an early manuscript set me to thinking more clearly about what exactly it was that I wanted to say to the reader. Kathie Jewell Briglia, M.S.W., and Kelly Hunt also contributed important details and insights. My former partner, Roberta Smith, M.D., was most helpful in ensuring that I had my bioethical facts correct. Jan Kirk offered suggestions for the title. The enthusiasm and kind words of my colleague Alan Spitzer, M.D., helped me through a period of doubt.

Other readers and early commentators on early drafts included Rabbi Raphael Gold, C. J. Alston, R.R.T., Gail Robinson, Diane Youmans, B.S.N., and Terri Eddy, R.N. Special thanks to Mary Ann Bowman Beil for her insistence that I continue to write, and to Gregg Stajich, Pharm.D., for constant kudos regarding the value of my undertaking for his students. I am grateful to Audrey Biloon for her constructive comments, especially as regards making the book less scientific and more readable. Our discussions were enjoyable and thought-provoking. I learned from our disagreements. To Gloria Nall Grizzle, Tracey and Brian Nease, and

Erin and Johnny Hinely, a special thank-you for their truthfulness and courage. I am sure I have left out some colleagues, and I apologize to them. I am most appreciative of everyone's help and advice.

And lastly, a great big thank-you to my husband, Steve, for putting me through medical school, supporting me through residency and fellowship, and enabling me to pursue a career that has brought me pleasure and a sense of accomplishment while doing "good" for babies.

Valley of Tiny Shadows

1

A Time to Live and a Time to Die

Ready and Willing

I was ready for the challenge. The year was 1975; this January night was my very first night on call in the neonatal intensive care unit (NICU). I was excited and filled with the same nervous anticipation I felt the night in May 1960 when I attended my first Spring Fling Dance at Central High School, a public school for academically gifted male students. A handsome sophomore on whom I had a terrible crush had asked me, a lowly freshman at the sister school Girls' High, to be his date. My mom, normally financially cautious, splurged and bought me a daffodil yellow Audrey Hepburn–style dress. It was sleeveless with a boat neck and a fitted bodice. Tiny pompoms adorned its hem. The dress was the prettiest and most costly one I had ever owned. Very excited and a little scared, I had awaited my escort's knock at our front door. Truth be known, I was consumed with a wicked sense of accomplishment. A year of well-planned secret flirtations at youth group meetings had finally yielded fruit. But a flood of doubts also deluged my brain. Would I have the grand time I'd imagined? More importantly, would I be ready for the challenge of dating this older man?

That night in the NICU my challenge was a world far removed from flirting with boys other than my date, worrying if I'm dressed grown-up enough for a high school dance, or obsessing about the appropriateness of a good-night kiss. I was midway through my second year of residency in pediatrics at Bradford Regional Hospital, a major academic teaching institution in Philadelphia. Although Bradford had a stellar reputation in the 1970's world of sick babies, it had yet to produce its first ventilated survivor under one kilogram (2 lbs. 3 oz.). But I didn't know that somber fact on my first night on call. Somehow the sobering statistic hadn't come up on teaching rounds led by the esteemed Dr. Beach as he dispensed pearls of wisdom to his admiring entourage of duckling-like residents, who hung onto every word he said.

Decked out in a shapeless scrub dress, yucky green, not daffodil yellow, and without pompoms, boatneck, or fitted bodice, I deemed myself ready for the adventures that night might bring. Thrilled to be starting my neonatal journey, I knew that after completing what would be a three-year pediatric residency, I'd begin a two-year fellowship in Perinatal-Neonatal Medicine. The extra training would be designed to teach me, in excruciating detail, all about the care of premature and sick newborns. After my training, at age thirty-three, I'd finally be able to start an independent professional life; it would be dedicated to saving those kinds of infants. That night on call was just the beginning of what I hoped would be a rewarding and noble career. Idealism ran rampant among us second-year residents who had managed to survive internship. Any sadness that came with not being able to save all the babies who would come under our care was far from our minds.

Since the early 1990's, facilities at most major teaching hospitals have included NICUs staffed around the clock by specialized neonatal nurses, nurse practitioners, respiratory therapists, pediatric residents (doctors still in specialty training), and neonatal fellows (doctors doing post-residency subspecialty training). Today, in the 24/7 digital age, an experienced attending physician is always available for consultation and advice, even for hands-on care. If a senior trained physician is not on site, his expertise is just a text message or a phone call away. In the 1970's and 80's, however, the level of expertise available in most NICUs plunged after hours. Night-shift staffing consisted of well-trained bedside nurses and an occasional respiratory therapist. The lowly pediatric resident, or sometimes even just an intern, often provided the highest level of medical knowledge and know-how for after-hours care. That night, the schedule declared that I was in charge.

Transport!

Shortly after I assumed call for that first night, the dedicated transport phone rang. It was a transport request! Another first!

"Okay, let's make sure I have this right. The baby is twelve weeks early. She's twenty-eight weeks gestation and weighs just over two pounds?"

"That's right, doctor," replied the nurse whose name I was told but didn't remember.

"Mom is an inpatient in your psychiatric ward?" I repeated what she had told me initially. Because my penmanship was almost illegible (a requisite for physicians it seems), and worse, my hand was shaking, I printed in block letters in the transport log. I was somewhat incredulous as the nurse on the other end of the phone line related even more sordid details surrounding the baby's birth. The patient's pregnancy had been known, but she had not complained of contractions. Neither the nurses nor the doctor suspected she was in labor, so she was admitted to the inpatient psychiatric floor for her primary psychiatric diagnosis, rather than to labor and delivery. A nurse's aid found the tiny infant afloat in a commode in the mother's room on the psychiatric ward soon after its birth. In addition to extreme prematurity, the baby nearly drowned and was exposed to a cold and grossly contaminated environment. The infant's attempted resuscitation outside the expertise of labor and delivery was a challenge.

Bizarre as it seems, this sequence of events is not as rare as one might think. The intense perineal pressure that an impending vaginal birth produces is a lot like the urge to have a bowel movement. On occasion mothers experience the urge to push before the doctors and nurses and sterile birthing equipment are ready. Talk about an irresistible force! Some mothers give birth precipitously with no time for the staff to set up properly for a delivery. Luckily, most of the time when a rapid delivery like that occurs, the baby enters the world onto a hospital bed, or in the delivery room, but without the usual elaborate preparations. From time to time the birth occurs in a less optimal place, such as on the living room sofa, in the family car or ambulance en route to the hospital, or in the emergency room. Sometimes the blessed event happens in a very public place, like at the local fast-food restaurant. In a few cases, as with this baby's birth, it occurs in the commode. The mother thinks she's going to have a bowel movement and doesn't realize that she's pushing out a baby instead.

We pediatric residents had a horrible name for such infants. We referred to them as "Ty-D-Bol babies" after the then-popular blue toilet-bowl cleaner. This term illustrates the morbid humor that keeps doctors, faced with sad and no-win situations, sane. Every pediatric and obstetrical resident knew exactly what was meant when an infant was declared a "Ty-D-Bol baby." There was no need for complex details with this kind of medical shorthand. Were we young doctors to have seriously contemplated this term and others like it, we would have been ashamed of having applied such unsavory, tasteless, inconsiderate, and unkind thoughts to our tiny patients. We would have surely been embarrassed and saddened that such vulgarities even crossed our minds as we cared for them. But being immature, eager, and inexperienced, and overwhelmed by the enormity of our task, we sank into our well-hidden feelings of isolation and inadequacy, not thinking before we spoke.

That first night on call I asked to speak with the referring doctor, which seemed like a reasonable request. I hoped to get the direct report without the nurse as an intermediary. Perhaps he might ask for some advice. Maybe I could make some semi-useful suggestions for ongoing care pending the arrival of our team. After all, at least for that night, I was the local expert on neonatal care.

The answer from the nurse was less than helpful. "He left for home forty-five minutes ago. Nothing more he can do anyway. We have no facilities to care for babies like this. We can't even get an intravenous line started in her, and we've tried five times. Please, come as fast as you can. We're just not used to caring for sick babies like this. We deal with normal-term infants. Taking care of babies like this one is *your* job, Dr. Sacks!"

It was the first time, but not the last, that I would hear this kind of feeble excuse during my residency and fellowship. Within thirty minutes of the call, our transport team left by ambulance for Walnut Hill Hospital, a small private facility just outside the greater metropolitan area. As I waited for the team to return to Bradford Regional with my first admission, I ran through the details of hyaline membrane disease, the most likely diagnosis for my tiny patient.

It was twelve years since President John F. Kennedy's infant son had succumbed to the condition of premature lungs, *or hyaline membrane disease (HMD)*, also known as *respiratory distress syndrome (RDS)* or *surfactant deficiency disease*. Patrick Bouvier Kennedy had been delivered by cesarian section on August 7, 1963, at Otis Air Force Base Hospital and had weighed just under five pounds. Born five and a half weeks early, his lungs had not yet sufficiently developed; specifically, they lacked surfactant, the viscous liquid that lines our lungs and prevents them from collapsing each time we exhale.

Think about blowing up party balloons. Remember how tough it is to get that initial inflation, how much force it requires when the diameter of the barely inflated balloon is small? Recall how much easier it becomes to inflate the balloon as it gets bigger, as the diameter of the balloon increases. This is what happens in the tiny air sacs *(alveoli)* of our lungs. As we exhale, air sacs in our lungs get smaller and therefore the pressure tending to collapse them increases. Inhaling air in order to inflate our lungs would be hard work without the presence of surfactant, which decreases the force tending to collapse our alveoli on exhalation.

In utero we don't need lungs or surfactant. The placenta is the organ of fetal respiration, and it is through the placenta that our mothers deliver oxygen to us and take care of getting rid of the carbon dioxide we produce in the uterus. Our lungs remain deflated before birth. By thirty-four weeks gestation (six weeks prior to the due date) most fetuses have developed surfactant and the ability to breathe on their own once they are born. Patrick, born too early, had not yet fully developed surfactant. His respiratory failure due to HMD progressed rapidly. Because Otis Air Force Base Hospital was not equipped to handle so sick an infant, his doctors transferred him to Boston Children's Hospital.

At that time pediatric knowledge and the therapeutic arsenal pediatricians had to fight HMD included only oxygen, antibiotics, intravenous fluids, and the provision of warmth in an incubator. Boston Children's Hospital also had a hyperbaric chamber that could deliver oxygen under pressure, but in 1963 none of those treatments was very effective for severe neonatal lung problems. Although doctors had known since 1959[1] that surfactant deficiency was the underlying cause of HMD, artificial surfactant would not be discovered nor approved for use for another thirty years.[2] Pediatricians at the Hospital for Sick Children in Toronto, Canada, were experimenting with the use of ventilators to save infants with severe HMD and other respiratory ailments, but those respirators were primitive by today's standards.[3] Today's modern mechanical respirators for neonates are of multiple varieties, sporting all kinds of bells, whistles, and alarms. If one particular ventilator isn't helping the baby, we try a ventilator that offers different controls and parameters.

Rumor had it that neonatal specialists in Toronto offered to transport and care for President Kennedy's baby, but that the offer had been declined. In retrospect, it isn't at all clear that the early type of ventilators in Toronto would have helped little Patrick, even if he would have survived that lengthy a transport. The baby remained hospitalized in Boston, where he died on his third day of life. An entire country mourned with the Kennedy family. Patrick's obituary in the *New York Times* pointed out that "the battle for the Kennedy baby was lost only because medical science has not yet advanced far enough to accomplish as quickly as necessary what the body can do by itself in its own time."[4] The experimental period in neonatology, which stimulated intensive research and ultimately incredible progress, can be traced directly to Patrick's tragic ending.[5]

Reviewing what I knew, the realization hit me—since the death of Patrick Kennedy, surprisingly little progress had been made in the care of sick newborns. In fact, the first Boards in Neonatal-Perinatal Medicine, recognizing Neonatology as a subspecialty of Pediatrics, would not be given until November of that year. Our therapeutic choices were certainly better and more numerous in 1975 than they were in 1963, as by 1975 we had jury-rigged adult ventilators for use in the neonate. But those machines were quite unsophisticated, as was the level of physicians' knowledge of how best to use them for babies. Most infants less than three pounds at birth or born earlier than two months prematurely still died if they were sick enough to need such crude, pieced-together machines.

On admission poor Janie M was bruised all over, especially on her legs. She was morbidly ill. Icy cold to the touch, she felt much like a defrosting chicken. Her rectal temperature was so low that it didn't register on our mercury thermometer. The only available treatment at our hospital—or any other for that matter—was provision of warmth, intravenous fluid, oxygen, unsophisticated antibiotics, a cardiac drug or two, and a prehistoric adult ventilator, which had been crudely outfitted for neonates. The ventilator was similar in appearance and sound to a pale green industrial-sized washing machine. In retrospect, I'm sure that it hadn't received FDA approval for use in neonates.[6]

Mr. M, Janie's father, had followed the ambulance back to the hospital. He stood by his baby's bedside as I attempted to explain the critical nature of her condition. I don't think I told him that she could die. In fact, I'm sure that I didn't say those words, "she could die." Those words were hard for me to say as a twenty-eight-year-old resident. They are still hard for me even today as a senior neonatologist.

Dad left. Actually, we didn't allow parents to stay at the bedside in 1975. That night I was thankful that the dad had gone to relieve the sitter at home with his other three young children. It's hard enough as a doctor or nurse to take care of a very sick infant without having to worry about the emotions of the parents as they watch their child's condition deteriorate. Parental presence is an added stressor to a fragile situation. Or so we thought in the early days of NICU care, as we placed our own insecurities before parental needs. Today parents are not only welcome in

NICUs, their presence is expected and encouraged. The team approach to neonatal treatment includes parents as well as professional staff.

Despite all of the orders I'd written (scribbled, actually), and which the nurses had dutifully carried out, the baby's condition deteriorated. By midnight Janie was on maximal respiratory support. *Dopamine*, a potent cardiac stimulating drug, ran through her intravenous line at the highest recommended rate to sustain her blood pressure and circulation. I'd threaded a flexible plastic catheter into her navel through her umbilical artery. That blood vessel once carried blood from Janie's heart back into the placenta to pick up oxygen and nutrients when she was safely harbored in her mother's womb. That night a catheter in that artery allowed me to withdraw samples of blood to test her clinical condition and assess her progress.

Among other parameters we tested the baby's blood gases. Blood gas measurements help doctors make an educated guess about how well a baby's lungs, heart, and circulation are functioning. We can follow the infant's progress (or lack of progress) in response to our treatments. We look at oxygen and *carbon dioxide* levels, and blood *pH*. This last parameter reflects the body's acid-base balance. Oxygen levels *(pO_2)* should be high enough to satisfy the body's critical need for oxygen, but not so high that they cause damage to eyes[7] and lungs.[8] The carbon dioxide level *(pCO_2)* indicates how well the lungs are eliminating carbon dioxide, the waste product of metabolism. We try to keep pCO_2 within safe bounds. Too low a pCO_2 decreases blood flow to the brain and has been associated with the development of *cerebral palsy* in infants. Too high a pCO_2 increases blood flow to the brain and can lead to a cerebral hemorrhage in very premature babies. No surprise—Janie's blood gases confirmed that she was not getting enough oxygen. Her elevated pCO_2 told us that gas exchange in her lungs was poor. Especially worrisome was her blood pH, the measure of acidity in her body.

Under baseline conditions, the human body keeps blood pH within very tight physiologic bounds. The brain, lung, and kidney function collaboratively to maintain these bounds. Our central respiratory drive (how frequently we take a spontaneous breath), combined with our lung-function, controls our carbon dioxide level. Over time our kidneys are able to absorb back into the circulation varying quantities of bicarbonate that would otherwise be wasted in our urine, thus balancing our pH. The human body is a magnificent machine. Evolution and/or Intelligent Design and/or the Deity have worked beautifully in fine-tuning our normally healthy bodies.

The normal range of pH is 7.35 to 7.45. The limits of acceptable pH for a sick preemie are 7.20 to 7.50. Because pH units are unique measurements based on logarithmic functions, the small drop of just 0.2 units, from 7.40 to 7.20, represents a *doubling* of the acid concentration. Physiologic processes do not function well at very low or very high pH.

Janie's pH was 6.72, a number not compatible with life for more than a few hours. She had been struck by a double whammy lowering her pH: her premature lungs weren't functioning, so carbon dioxide was accumulating, lowering her pH, and she had also developed a buildup of *lactic acid*, the end product of anaerobic (without oxygen) metabolism. When the availability of oxygen to the cells is critically compromised, the body reverts to a much less efficient process, which uses more glucose and less oxygen, and produces lactic acid as the end product.[9] The large concentration of lactic acid also had another deadly source: Janie probably had suffered a massive brain hemorrhage, a frequent occurrence in tiny, critically ill, unstable infants. Brain hemorrhages are often accompanied by a buildup of lactic acid, which further lowers the blood's pH. The level of oxygen in Janie's blood was way too low to provide the oxygen she needed. Unfortunately her heart was also failing and was not delivering even that very low level of oxygen to the cells of her vital organs. Her tissues were starving for oxygen; they were in the dying process. Janie was in the dying process.

As a young doctor, I didn't recognize that condition.

A Real Challenge

The baby's nurse handed me a slip of paper testifying to the alarming blood-gas results. Trained to think in algorithmic terms, I believed there had to be a medical step-by-step solution to every medical problem; one must simply drill down deep enough in the algorithm and choose the right pathway. My training as a pediatric resident had not included learning to deal with impending death as the end result of the pathway.

Janie was already on the highest ventilator settings she could tolerate. There was no way to blow off more carbon dioxide through ventilator manipulation without risking rupture of her stiff lungs. I decided that the alternative remedy, a dose of sodium bicarbonate, would be a quick, albeit temporary fix for her critical status.

My tiny patient decided otherwise. Her monitor alarm went off, beeping and flashing. In front of my eyes, she *coded*, which is medical jargon for a heart rate falling to dangerously low levels or even to zero, and cessation of spontaneous breathing. Her skin color was pale, ashen blue-gray, and her circulation was poor to say the least. Janie appeared lifeless, and indeed would be dead within minutes if not resuscitated quickly. Treatment would consist of rapidly raising the oxygen levels and simultaneously lowering the carbon dioxide levels. This could be done by increasing ventilation with pure oxygen, initiating external cardiac massage, and jump-starting the heart by administration of *adrenalin*. If all of that failed, sodium bicarbonate would be given to neutralize the lactic acid that had accumulated through poor tissue perfusion with oxygen-poor blood. Additional fluid to increase circulation would then follow. Although all of that was not yet necessary, I had to think ahead. A-B-C-D: airway, breathing, circulation, drugs. Mnemonics can help physicians remember what to do in critical situations.

As the doctor in charge that night, I calmly (at least I hoped I looked calm) "called the code," and began to hyperventilate the infant as I'd been taught to do. I'm barely five feet tall. Since the height of the early vintage radiant warmers on which we cared for infants was not yet adjustable, to reach the baby comfortably I had to stand on a small stool. I used an ambu bag, ventilating at rates faster than the primitive respirator could attain. This was my first all-by-myself code. Hesitantly I asked the nurses to assist by providing external cardiac massage while I took care of breathing for the baby. I then ordered a dose of intravenous adrenalin. To my disappointment those measures failed to revive her. My brain moved to the next step. According to the medical texts I had studied, the next maneuver was to give bicarbonate. I administered the recommended dose, followed by more fluid and another adrenalin chaser.

Seven minutes into this frenzied activity, miraculously, the baby's heart rate finally rose from 50 to 120 beats per minute, the lower limit of normal for a small newborn. At this point Janie ceased to be a baby in my immature resident eyes. She would be either my success or my failure. It was no longer about her; it was about me and my skills as a doctor. It would be several more years of training before I learned the art of putting a patient's best interests ahead of my ego.

My heart pounded in my own chest. Adrenalin began circulating through my veins. A true life-or-death situation and I was in charge. Just fourteen months out of medical school and someone else's life was literally in my hands! The rush sensation was not completely unpleasant. Well on my way to becoming an adrenalin junky, I savored the excitement of an emergency, if it was to have a successful outcome. But I was very nervous and hoped I didn't look as nervous and inexperienced as I felt. How I wished I could have called an attending for help, or maybe just for reassurance that I was doing all I could do. But that wasn't how it was done in Academia in 1975. A phone call would have been a sign of weakness or ignorance and at 1:00 A.M. might even have angered the more experienced senior physician. I rationalized that consulting with someone more experienced wouldn't have made any difference anyway, since my patient had almost no chance of recovery. This was a true learning experience. I was completely on my own.

The baby was still alive, so the code must have been a success. On reexamination, she looked awful, even worse than she had when she had been admitted a few hours before. Her *fontanel*, the soft spot on the top of her head, was no longer soft. The one-by-two-centimeter area was very hard, almost bulging. This was not a good sign. I suspected that because of the circumstances of her birth, her lung problems, and resuscitative efforts, she had suffered a brain hemorrhage or stroke. Her brain was swollen with blood that caused increased pressure within her head, reflected in the hardening of her fontanel. Since bedside cranial ultrasound, today's standard means of diagnosing neonatal brain hemorrhage had not yet been invented, I ordered a *hematocrit*, a measure of the percentage of red blood cells in Janie's blood. If she had sustained a large cerebral hemorrhage, the blood loss would have been reflected in a lower hematocrit. While this test wouldn't confirm a hemorrhage, a low hematocrit would have been highly suggestive. In 1975 a large brain hemorrhage in a very premature baby almost always meant the baby would not survive. Anxiously I awaited the results.

It never crossed my mind to call the baby's father to update him on the downturn in her course. Shouldn't he have known that his tiny daughter was dying? Whether he would have wanted to be with her, to hold and comfort her as she died was not a question I asked myself, although it should have been. Circumstances of training in the 1970's made communication with parents a low priority, and a skill I was forced to learn over years of practice through reading and clinical experience. There were no lectures on that sort of topic until at least ten years later. With notable rare exceptions, attending physicians did not teach communication skills by example. Today we actively teach medical students and residents the importance of communication with parents. Since 2005, communication has been one of the six core competencies for the modern physician in training in all specialties.

One hour later as the panic-value hematocrit result was called back from the lab, the baby coded again. I jumped into action, somewhat more confident than before. As we used to say in medicine (before the report from the Institute for Organized Medicine accused the medical establishment of killing 45,000 to 98,000 patients each year through medical errors): "See one, do one, teach one."[10] I was up to "teach one."

A few more rounds of drugs during a ten-minute resuscitation succeeded in raising the baby's heart rate. My poor patient was no longer making any efforts to breathe. She was in sync with the ventilator. She was no longer responding to my touch or moving spontaneously. Worse, her hematocrit was reported back as a dangerously low twenty percent, less than half of what it should have been. The presumptive conclusion was that she had sustained a major brain hemorrhage. In the unlikely event that she survived her breathing problems, she would face significant developmental delay, neurological problems, and profound intellectual deficits.

I ordered a blood transfusion to restore her hematocrit to more normal levels. She would die in "Harvard balance"—all her numbers within the correct ranges, an accomplishment of which any resident should be proud. Beyond that treatment there was nothing more I could offer.

It's going to be a long night, I thought to myself as I headed to the sleep room to catch a few minutes of rest.

I never made it to the bed. Janie coded a third time in as many hours. Now really into the NICU routine—after all, this was to be my life's work—I stepped back up on my stool and confidently barked out orders to the bedside nurse.

"More adrenalin! Another round of bicarbonate! Keep up the cardiac massage!"

The nurses couldn't move fast enough to please me; their facial expressions told me they knew my feelings. I couldn't control my therapeutic frenzy. I hadn't yet learned to recognize my out-of-self-control Energizer Bunny mode. I'd not yet learned to maintain calm during a crisis. Risa, a middle-aged nurse with fifteen years' experience in neonatal intensive care, was the charge nurse that evening. She approached me. In my hyperexcited don't-you-know-I'm-in-charge-here state I failed to notice her. Standing behind me, Risa gripped my shoulder with a firm hand and softly said, "Dr. Sacks, stop. You don't have to resuscitate the baby again. It's over. She's dying. Nothing you can do will change that. Don't make her suffer any more. It's over. Please, just stop the resuscitation. It's really okay to stop."

I was stunned. As the blood drained from my face, I felt that sick punched-in-the-solar-plexus sensation in my gut. I was shocked at Risa's chutzpah as well as her calm demeanor. How dare she criticize me! This was definitely not how I pictured my career. I envisioned babies rescued from the brink of death, thankful parents, and admiring and appreciative staff. I was going into neonatology to save lives, not to give up so easily.

Was Janie suffering? Do babies really suffer? I thought preemies couldn't feel pain. How did Risa know something I didn't? And anyway, wasn't the doctor—that's me, big-man-on-campus, second-year resident—supposed to call the shots? Nurses telling me, the doctor, what to do? Wasn't it ordained somewhere in the bible of Medical Rules that the doctor gets to decide when enough is enough? I felt compelled to respond to this challenge to my authority and knowledge.

"What do you mean, stop? Resuscitation worked before! She came back! As long as her heart rate recovers with cardiac massage and drugs, why shouldn't I continue? Isn't this what we do here in the NICU? We save babies. We don't just let them die!"

At least not, please God, on my first night on call.

"Just leave her alone," Risa calmly replied, quietly but with determination, looking straight into my eyes. Clearly Risa had confronted more than one pediatric resident in her career.

"Enough is enough. I know you mean well, doctor, but you can't help her anymore. Believe me, I've seen this many times, with residents far more experienced than you. Nothing we do here will make a difference in this baby's outcome. We're not saving her life, we're just prolonging her dying. Trust me, it's okay to let her go peacefully. Please, just stop all this beating on her chest and rounds of medication. It's not helping; it's only hurting and causing her pain. Can't you see that? Please, doctor, let her die in peace."

Risa got no verbal reply from me. The lump in my throat precluded all speech. I bit my lip and offered a silent prayer that I wouldn't cry in front of the nurses. Stepping down from my perch, I backed away from the bedside and nodded my agreement to Risa. Utterly defeated, I turned my back to the baby. I wasn't sure that I could take anymore nights like this, let alone a career full of nights like this.

Ego deflated, heavy-hearted, eyes brimming over, I left the messy details of a dying baby to Risa, and I headed to the resident's sleep room to have a good cry. Alone.

1. M. E. Avery and J. Mead, "Surface Properties in Relation to Atelectasis and Hyaline Membrane Disease." *American Journal of Diseases of Children* 97 (1959): 517–23.

2. T. Fujiwara, M. Konishi, S. Chida, et al. (The Surfactant-TA Study Group), "Surfactant Replacement Therapy With a Single Postventilatory Dose of a Reconstituted Bovine Surfactant in Preterm Neonates With Respiratory Distress Syndrome: Final Analysis of a Multicenter, Double-blind, Randomized Trial and Comparison With Similar Trials." *Pediatrics* 86 (1990): 753–64.

3. M. Delivoria-Papadopoulos and P. R. Swyer, "Assisted Ventilation in Terminal Hyaline Membrane Disease." *Archives of Disease in Childhood* 39 (1964): 481–84.

4. *New York Times*, August 10, 1963.

5. P. L. Toubas, "Truth Is a Corrected Error." *Journal of Perinatology* 23 (2003): 1–2.

6. Prior to 1979, medical devices were not regulated. Congress passed the Medical Device Amendments Act in 1976 to ensure safety and effectiveness of medical devices, including diagnostic products. The two questionably safe devices that accelerated such legislation were defective cardiac pacemakers and the Dalkon Shield contraceptive device. The amendments require manufacturers to register with FDA and follow quality control procedures. Some products must have premarket approval by FDA; others must meet performance standards before marketing. The 1976 amendments defined devices similarly to drugs, but noted that drugs cause a chemical reaction in the body, whereas devices do not. They called for all devices to be divided into classes, with varying amounts of control required in each one. All medical devices for neonates must have FDA approval.

7. High levels of oxygen in the blood can damage the vessels of the developing retina and lead to visual problems, even to retinal detachment and blindness. *Retrolental fibroplasia (RLF)*, now more properly called *retinopathy of prematurity (ROP)*, was once the leading cause of childhood blindness in the United States. By 1953 nearly 10,000 American children had lost their sight on account of the largely *iatrogenic* disease. Although prematurity is the sine qua non for susceptibility to ROP, it was the unlimited exposure to excessive concentrations of oxygen in the 1940's and 1950's, made possible by newer airtight incubators, that caused the epidemic of ROP in surviving premature infants.

8. Exposure of the lungs to high concentrations of oxygen, even in adults, causes lung inflammation and cellular changes. Preterm infants lack antioxidant protection. They are prone to rapid development of permanent changes in lung structure and function when placed in oxygen-enriched environments. We call these changes *bronchopulmonary dysplasia (BPD)*. Even today, with tighter control of oxygen exposure and direct measurement of blood levels of oxygen tension and oxygen saturation, BPD is responsible for increased morbidity and mortality in extremely premature infants who survive beyond the first few weeks and months of life.

9. With inadequate oxygen, mitochondrial metabolism abandons the efficient Krebs cycle (nemesis of anyone who ever took a biochemistry course) and reverts to a much less efficient process that consumes more fuel (glucose) and produces lactic acid as the end product. Muscle cells normally do this on a temporary basis when we exercise hard. The muscle discomfort we feel with severe exertion is attributable to this localized buildup of lactic acid.

10. Linda T. Kohn, Janet M. Corrigan, and Molla S. Donaldson, eds, *To Err Is Human: Building a Safer Health System* (Washington, D.C.: Committee on Quality of Healthcare in America, Institute of Medicine, National Academy Press, 2000).

2

JONATHAN'S MIRACLE

A Mother's Love

It was the spring of 1984. Jonathan W was a slightly preterm white male infant who weighed in at four pounds ten ounces at his birth. According to his mother, his name in Hebrew meant *gift from God*. From the moment of birth it was clear that Jonathan was not a normal newborn. To begin with, his mother's much-desired first pregnancy had been complicated by *polyhydramnios*, a word derived as many other medical words, from Greek. *Poly* means *much*, and *hydramnios* means *water*. *Polyhydramnios* is the term obstetricians use to indicate that too much amniotic fluid has accumulated in the pregnant uterus. Polyhydramnios makes the pregnant woman physically uncomfortable, bigger than she should be for any given length of pregnancy. To her chagrin she may look like she is due to deliver any day, yet she may still have two to three months to go. She gets tired of responding to: *"Are you sure you're not further along?" "You look awfully big!" "You must be carrying a ten pounder!"* Polyhydramnios may also signify a threat to the well-being of her fetus. When the uterus is stretched by excess fluid to full-term size several weeks before the baby's due date, preterm labor may ensue. The uterus can simply not hold any more volume and begins to contract. Most significantly for the fetus, polyhydramnios may be the result of a serious fetal condition: intestinal blockage, or neurological impairment as Jonathan's case turned out to be.[1]

It was noted on his last ultrasound, a week before his birth, that Jonathan was in a breech position. That meant he was upside-down in the uterus. With his buttocks, instead of his head, sitting above the cervix, this position spelled problems for his delivery. A baby's head is larger than its butt and acts as a battering ram in the birth canal. Once the relatively large head passes through the open cervix and vaginal canal, the rest of the infant follows easily, as it is narrower in girth than his head is. Because the feet or buttocks are delivered first in a breech vaginal delivery, the head, having larger dimensions compared to the feet or butt, may become entrapped by the cervix. From the neck downward the baby is out, but the head remains in the uterus with the muscular cervix clamped down around the fetus's neck. Since the umbilical cord passes through the same cervical opening alongside the head, it too is entrapped and compressed, possible cutting off circulation through the umbilical cord to the infant. Lack of oxygen can potentially lead to brain or other organ damage, which may or may not be reversible. Cesarian section for a breech presentation helps to alleviate this potentially life-threatening situation. Since the early 1980's, cesarian delivery has become the norm for breech presentation. Most practicing obstetricians under fifty years of age have had little experience with vaginal breech deliveries. Unless current standards change, today's residents in obstetrics will acquire limited experience in delivering vaginal breech births. Soon this critical obstetrical skill may be a lost art. When that happens, no one will be able to deliver a breech birth in the few acceptable indications for a vaginal breech delivery, such as smaller second twin, or in situations where performing a cesarian section is impossible. Mrs. W's obstetrician advised her to undergo a cesarian section for the sake of the baby's well-being, and she consented.

The baby's problems, however, continued after the delivery. Jonathan was just not right. He had abnormal positioning of his arms and legs, with contractures of his joints. His knees were locked in hyperextension and did not bend. His left arm was permanently flexed at the elbow, and his right arm was hyperextended and was also difficult to bend. His fingers deviated to the inner or radial side of his wrist. His feet were severely clubbed. His muscles controlling his hips were tight, and his hips did not spread open completely. Changing his diaper was a challenge.

Multiple contractures have many causes. In Jonathan's case the condition was likely due to his failure to move regularly during in-utero development because of an abnormal central nervous system. His improperly developed brain didn't send the right signals to his muscles to tell them to alternately contract and relax throughout his eight-month tenure in the womb. His limbs stiffened before birth, and he remained in a breech position instead of turning head down for delivery. His poorly developed brain also did not allow him to develop a normal swallowing function, and he did not swallow the amniotic fluid as it formed. Hence, it accumulated in his mother's uterus and polyhydramnios resulted.

Jonathan's facial features were unusual as well. He was decidedly odd looking. Jonathan suffered from a cleft lip and palate. His ears were set on his head too low vis-à-vis the position of his eyes. They were also rotated backward about forty-five degrees. His eyes were too close together, a medical condition called *hypotelorism*. Mild degrees of hypotelorism are not considered abnormal. Jonathan's case was not mild.

We heard a heart murmur just to the right and one inch below Jonathan's left nipple. Heart murmurs in newborns are common. Studies have shown that if we listen to newborn hearts every hour, which we don't normally do, we would find that almost fifty percent of babies will have an innocent murmur noted sometime during the first few days of life. But Jonathan was not just an ordinary baby. He had multiple abnormalities. In such a newborn the presence of two or more abnormal features makes it likely that a third will be found. In Jonathan's case we suspected congenital heart disease and ordered an *echocardiogram* (ultrasound of the heart). The test revealed a moderate-sized *ventricular septal defect*, a large hole between the two pumping chambers of Jonathan's heart. Thankfully, the hole didn't seem to cause Jonathan any problems at that point.

When one inserts a gloved finger into a term-newborn's mouth, the baby reflexively begins to suck and swallow. This maneuver with

Jonathan's mouth revealed that he lacked both suck and swallow reflexes. In a normal infant these primitive reflexes appear early in gestation and they originate in the most primitive sections of the brain. Their absence in a close-to-term infant is a very bad sign. Jonathan's failure to develop a suck-and-swallow reflex caused the polyhydramnios that his mother had developed.

No sucking and swallowing in a mature infant equals a brain abnormality until proven otherwise. I ordered a CAT scan of Jonathan's brain, and unfortunately our hunch was confirmed. Jonathan had a severe developmental problem called *holoprosencephaly*.[2] We knew that this abnormality meant Jonathan's life expectancy was limited and his outlook for normal development was zero. Over the course of the first few days of Jonathan's life, I gently shared this information in small doses with his family.

The W family was not repulsed by Jonathan's condition. Far from it. They continued to love Jonathan despite his problems. They came from rural Georgia, and had deep abiding faith in God's power to heal. They were given to unabashed praising of the Lord for the good things with which they felt their lives were blessed. They firmly believed in God's capacity to perform miracles. Intellectually they had a fair understanding of their little boy's problems and the dim future he faced, but they believed that if they prayed hard enough, Jesus could and likely would send a miracle to cure Jonathan's condition. Georgia after all is firmly in the Bible belt, forming its slightly off-center buckle.

Having recently arrived in the South from the self-proclaimed more rational North, where one's religious beliefs were not commonly shared in a public forum, I found myself facing this type of religious fervor daily. I didn't fight it, and I tried hard not to roll my eyes in response to parental comments about God's healing power superseding medical expertise and hard medical reality. In my fifteen months in the South, I'd already learned, if not to embrace extreme (to my mind) religious attitudes, at least to acknowledge, tolerate, and even respect them. Although I didn't know it at the time, life in the deep South would ultimately profoundly change me, including my religious beliefs. Slowly but surely my own metamorphosis would occur. But I would never learn to like grits. There were going to be limits to my cultural change.

Jonathan's mother spent hours each day rocking him, singing to him, *loving on him* (in the Southern vernacular). She was a fixture in the NICU.

Dilemma

Jonathan's digestive tract was not able to absorb formula feedings. As with all high-risk infants who are unable to tolerate breast milk or formula feedings, Jonathan received a complex *intravenous* solution called *hyper-alimentation* or *total parenteral nutrition (TPN)*. This clear yellow solution contains sugar, minerals, vitamins, and elemental hydrolyzed protein. Fats are delivered in a milky-white companion solution called Intralipid. Developed in the late 1960's by a pediatric surgeon in Philadelphia, TPN has saved the lives of hundreds of thousands of children, especially tiny premature infants and babies who require complex abdominal or cardiac surgery.[3] This golden-colored solution is expensive; each bag of TPN is customized for the needs of its recipient and must be assembled sterilely in the pharmacy under a *laminar flow hood*. Because of its high cost at the time, some ethicists considered its use heroic, and therefore would limit its utilization in circumstances they deemed futile. Jonathan had been unable to digest formula feedings and had required TPN for ten days so far. We wondered if his digestive system would ever begin to work well enough to absorb nutrition. If we could never get him to tolerate any kind of formula feedings through his bowel, and if he was headed for long-term support on intravenous nutrition, would further TPN be considered futile in light of his neurological issues?

After intense discussion among the three neonatologists and the one pediatric surgeon on the staff, we decided to challenge Jonathan's gastrointestinal tract one more time. If he could accept specialty formula feedings through a *nasogastric tube*, we would be able to gradually discontinue TPN and proceed with placement of a permanent *gastrostomy tube* for feedings. Since Jonathan could neither suck nor swallow, he would never be able to eat in the normal sense of the word, and a gastrostomy tube could bypass that problem. However, if Jonathan couldn't even absorb his nutrition, even with a predigested formula placed artificially into his stomach, we would have to discuss withdrawal of TPN support with his family, because long-term TPN was not a reasonable treatment for Jonathan, given his overall condition. We hoped it wouldn't come to that point.

We restarted Jonathan's feedings. We were, or more appropriately, Jonathan was, successful in absorbing formula fed to him through a temporary tube placed through his nose into his stomach. Three weeks into his hospitalization, Jonathan's level of support had been reduced to non-heroic requirements for warmth and nourishment with tube feedings of elemental formula. He was unchanged neurologically despite daily sessions of physical therapy to his limbs. He would never learn to suck from a bottle. His overall development would never progress beyond that of a newborn baby and his lifespan would be severely limited. We had repeated discussions with his family about what course would be in Jonathan's best long-term interests, and about what we should do if he should stop breathing or his heartbeat should cease. Finally I raised the issue of a Do Not Resuscitate order with the W family.

"Jonathan will continue to receive ongoing care, nutrition, medications, and all comfort measures," I explained. "We will be sure that he doesn't suffer. However, in the event he stops breathing, or his heart rate falls, we will not attempt to resuscitate him."

Mom nodded in agreement.

"He will not be subjected to placing a breathing tube in his windpipe, and we won't hook him up to a ventilator. If Jonathan begins to breathe again on his own, he will live. If he does not breathe, he . . ."

"He'll go to be with Jesus," interrupted his mother.

I documented our discussion in Jonathan's chart, and the family's agreement with the DNR order.

To his family's heartfelt delight, and the medical and nursing staff's relief, Jonathan remained so stable that we did not expect him to die while he was still hospitalized. We anticipated he would need a gastrostomy tube, so he could be safely fed by his parents, but we also anticipated eventual discharge to home, which was exactly what his family wanted. So far, their faith and prayers had paid off. Jonathan was still alive. Perhaps a real miracle would still happen.

Attempts to introduce bottle feedings to Jonathan continued, but as we anticipated, they were unsuccessful. Jonathan could not suck from a bottle, much less coordinate sucking, swallowing, and breathing, necessary skills for oral feeding. After much dialogue about the pros and cons of a gastrostomy tube *(G-tube)*, Jonathan's parents finally agreed to surgical insertion of a permanent G-tube. With a G-tube they would be able to feed him at home with a measure of ease and safety. Should Jonathan merit a heavenly miracle granting him the skill to coordinate sucking and swallowing and breathing in sequence, the G-tube could be removed without further surgical intervention. The doctor could simply deflate the balloon that keeps the tube in place and pull out the tube. The entrance site would seal over naturally.

The simple G-tube surgery went smoothly. After the operation Jonathan tolerated G-tube feedings well. The nurses taught Mrs. W how to set up Jonathan's tube feedings. Hopes for homecoming were in the air, but one sticky problem remained. Jonathan could not maintain a normal body temperature in an open crib, even with clothes, a cap, and three blankets on him.

About this time we received the results of Jonathan's *metabolic screening*, which had been drawn when he was three days old. The findings were abnormal: the state lab reported no detectable level of *thyroid hormone* or *thyroid stimulating hormone (TSH)*. These unusual and alarming labs were consistent with failure of Jonathan's pituitary gland to develop at the base of his brain. Hypothyroid infants have difficulty with regulating body temperature, may feed poorly, are constipated, and ultimately, if not treated, become severely retarded. Jonathan's lack of thyroid hormone explained his inability to maintain body temperature in an open bassinet. Although he had grown to over six pounds, he still could not hold up his body temperature above ninety-six degrees without the assistance of an incubator or radiant warmer. My associate, Dr. William Greystone, in a fit of I-dotting and T-crossing from which he frequently suffered, requested an endocrinology consultation for Jonathan to advise him how to manage the baby's hypothyroidism.

What was the point of straightening out Jonathan's thyroid status? He was going to die no matter what, wasn't he? If his intellectual developmental potential was already nil, it couldn't be any worse if we failed to correct his thyroid problem. On the one hand, looking at temperature maintenance as a comfort measure, one might argue that we needed to determine how much synthetic thyroid hormone Jonathan required so that he could be transitioned to an open bassinet and might be able to maintain his temperature. On the other hand, we could have empirically prescribed a dose of thyroid replacement hormone based on Jonathan's weight, and monitored his temperature regulation. Of course we could have done nothing and allowed Jonathan to maintain a subnormal body temperature. I suspected that Dr. Greystone was concerned over how the medical record would appear if a serious resolvable problem remained unresolved. Hence his request for consultation.

Mrs. W had just finished holding and rocking Jonathan, and had put him back down on the warming bed. Although the temperature probe was back in place, the heart and *apnea* monitor leads had been discontinued on account of Jonathan's DNR status. Mrs. W was on her way out of the unit. It was lunchtime and perhaps she was headed to the cafeteria. Unfortunately she was still standing at the doorway of the unit, twenty feet from Jonathan's bedside when the endocrinologist, Dr. Ali Abilove, arrived to consult on Jonathan's thyroid issues.

As medical students, future doctors learn to listen first to the heart and lungs in babies if the baby is quiet. Poking the bellies of babies often leads to crying, and then one cannot appreciate the heart sounds nor evaluate air entry in the lungs. Jonathan was quiet, very quiet, and the endocrinologist began his examination by placing his stethoscope on Jonathan's chest.

Ali was Iranian and had enormous dark eyes. As he listened, his prominent jet black eyes grew larger when he heard no detectable heart rate! He listened again. Still no heart rate. Jonathan was not breathing. Jonathan had died.

The Miracle

At some point after the nurse had recorded Jonathan's last set of vital signs, Jonathan had slipped away without fanfare, probably while resting comfortably in the loving security of his mother's arms.

Now quite agitated, but recognizing that Jonathan's mother was aware of all that was going on from her position in the doorway, Dr. Abilove motioned for the nurse, Peggy, to come to the bedside. Peggy quickly explained Jonathan's DNR status to the endocrine consultant. She also confirmed that Jonathan was pulseless. Visibly shaken, Dr. Abilove quickly departed.

My colleague Dr. Cynthia James was paged STAT (which means emergency, come now!). Dr. James came in the back way steering clear of any anxious parents who might have been waiting in ambush at the front door. Per Fire Marshal's rules, all NICUs have at least two entrances/exits. The extra door in or out can be misused as a staff escape hatch, providing a way to avoid families. By now Jonathan's leads were reconnected to the monitor, confirming that there was no cardiac activity, not even a solitary white blip on the dark screen. Dr. James pronounced Jonathan deceased and then turned to the doorway to talk with Jonathan's mother.

Reading Dr. James's face, Mrs. W suddenly understood what had happened. She began to wail loudly. The disturbance, but not the grief, had to be contained, so as not to upset other families in the unit. Dr. James led the mother and her newly deceased baby into the tiny residents' room that adjoined the NICU. We often took families to this room after a neonatal death for a private sympathetic discussion with grieving parents. A noisy open NICU or a hallway offers no privacy. Placing portable curtains around the bedside (as circumstances often forced us to do) certainly helped, but the acute grief was still a semipublic spectacle. Such a scene was uncomfortable for the affected parents, but especially for the other families in the unit. Subsequent newer units constructed in the twenty-first century will have private rooms or cubicles for each tiny patient, and a folding bed or comfortable chair for the parents. One day sick baby and parent privacy will be a value we will honor not only with lip service but also with construction dollars.

I had been at lunch when the crisis had occurred. Returning to the NICU, I noted that Jonathan's radiant warmer bed was suddenly empty.

"Where's the baby? Where's Jonathan?" I asked, alarmed.

"Jonathan passed," Peggy told me. Without further comment she directed me to the on-call room where Jonathan's mother and Dr. James had retreated.

What happened next was the strangest neonatal death scene I have ever experienced. Picture the tableau. An eight-by-ten windowless room with an unmade bunk bed shoved against one wall. A solitary desk chair sat in the middle of the room, but without a desk. Mrs. W was seated in the chair facing sideways toward the bed, tenderly clutching a hospital blanket in which she held Jonathan close to her chest. Her loud wailing had been reduced to soft crying. Dr. James, my colleague, dear friend, and an experienced neonatologist, was seated on the lower bunk, speaking softly to her.

Shortly after I started working in this Southern NICU, in the course of a conversation about a newborn who had recently died, I complimented Dr. James on the way she dealt with bereaved parents after babies died. It is a truly difficult task. We know the science of grieving, the stages of grief. Elisabeth Kübler-Ross described them in her pioneering work.[4] We also know there is an art to dealing with parents who have lost their precious babies. In the modern developed world, neonatal death occurs infrequently. An uncomfortable subject, death had not been dealt with directly at all during my pediatric residency and neonatal fellowship. Perhaps the physician's role in consoling a parent cannot really be taught in lecture form. Sometimes we can learn by example and apprenticeship, but more often physicians in training never master the how-to's. While a doctor who has not personally experienced the pain of losing a child cannot know exactly how the parents feel, he or she must nevertheless try to exhibit some appropriate emotional response. Parents want to believe that the doctors and nurses care, that their infant's death has meaning, and that their child's life had meaning. Grieving parents see through a charade of niceties. They value sincerity. Regardless of the quality of relationship a physician has with the family, it is always appropriate to say, "I wish there was more we could have done to help your baby." That sentiment is always true.

Although she knew I was there, Dr. James would not make eye contact with me. She was aware that I had been monitoring Jonathan's care as much as she had. She knew I had spoken on a daily basis with Mrs. W. Dr. James appreciated how much I admired her technique with families after a neonatal death; we'd discussed it more than once. I'd told her how I was counting on continuing to better my own skills from her example. Nevertheless, Dr. James would not look directly at me, not even for a fleeting moment.

Continuing to direct her gaze and comments to Jonathan's mother, she softly said, "No, I don't know how much longer. This is very unusual, Mrs. W." Dr. James gently touched Jonathan's mother on the arm.

"I'll admit I've never seen this before, that's why I can't tell you what will happen. I just don't know. Why don't I let you and Jonathan be alone together for a while. I'll have the nurses call the rest of your family. I'm sure they'd want to be here."

Jonathan's mother nodded in silent agreement, then turned her loving gaze back to her baby and continued sobbing quietly.

Without another word Dr. James motioned me out of the room. She guided me by the elbow silently down the short hallway all the way around the corner to the labor and delivery suite. By now I was really puzzled. What had happened? What was so unusual? How much longer for what?

Before I could begin to question the strange scenario I had just witnessed, Dr. James blurted out, "Linda, when Ali came to consult on the absent thyroid function, he was the one who discovered that Jonathan had no heart rate and wasn't breathing. That's how Ali found him. They tell me it wasn't a pretty scene. I mean, we expected that Jonathan could die at any time, but he seemed to be stable. I guess we didn't expect to just find him dead! Or for a consultant to find him dead! Peggy paged me STAT because they didn't know what else to do. After all, he did have a DNR order in place, so there was no resuscitation to be done. When we hooked Jonathan up to the monitor, he was flat lining. Not even a weak blip on the screen."

"Oh, my God!" I exclaimed, glad it wasn't me who found Jonathan.

"To make matters worse, his mother was standing in the doorway. She must have guessed what had happened because she started to cry pretty loudly. I tried to calm her down. I thought she'd like to hold Jonathan again, so I took her into the residents' room so she could hold her baby. You know how I like to do this. Well, she was nestling him close and keening over him"—Dr. James illustrated with a phantom baby—"you do know what keening is, don't you—"

"Yeah, I know what keening is, like in Zorba the Greek. Wailing over the dead or dying."

"Then we heard a whooshing sound," Dr. James said. " 'I heard him breathe,' Mrs. W whispered to me," she continued. " 'No, he's not breathing. Jonathan's gone,' " I told her. " 'You must have hugged him so tightly that the air in his lungs was pushed out. It only sounded like he was breathing. It happens naturally sometimes. I'm so sorry, Mrs. W, I know you were hoping for a miracle, that you wanted to take him home. I'm so sorry, Jonathan is gone.' "

"Then I heard it myself," Dr. James continued. " '*Ooosh.*' " Jonathan made that sound again. And again. And again. '*Ooosh, ooosh, ooosh.*' "

"I didn't even have a stethoscope with me! Who knew I would need one? I had to have Peggy bring me one. I checked him with the stethoscope, and he had a heart rate of fifty, and he was breathing very shallowly and very slowly."

Her blue-gray eyes grew larger. I was spellbound.

"Linda, he'd been dead for at least thirty minutes! I swear it was thirty minutes! Electrically dead! No activity on the monitor. I couldn't believe it! Not knowing what was going on, I told his mother that this situation is very unusual, and I didn't know how long Jonathan would continue to rally. That's the point when you walked in. Sorry I couldn't acknowledge your presence. There was no way I could explain the situation to you without breaking the magical spell in the room. It was all so strange, so unexpected, so, so . . . weird. This has never happened to me before. I don't know how to explain it medically, but I do know that Mrs. W didn't need to hear the story retold. I hope you understand."

I did. I returned to the residents' room and opened the door. Mrs. W was still rocking Jonathan, who was still breathing! Within a few minutes the entire family—mom, dad, grandmothers, grandfathers, great-grandmother, Aunt Mazie, Uncle Jake, and several others whose names I didn't catch—all crowded into the room to be with the baby as he transitioned from that other world, to this world, and then on to the next. Jonathan lived for another three hours, spending it cradled in loving relatives' arms, and being passed tenderly from one person to the other. I checked in on the scene every fifteen to twenty minutes. When Jonathan finally ceased breathing, I waited a full thirty minutes before checking his heart rate again. There would be no repeat performance. Apologetically, and with as much compassion as this newly displaced Northerner could muster, I told the assembled group that Jonathan was finally gone.

"Jesus needed another rose for his garden, and he chose Jonathan," Aunt Mazie pronounced, tears in her eyes.

The family nodded in agreement. I marveled at their faith; part of me envied their trust in the Almighty. There were no Amens. The only acknowledgment of Aunt Mazie's declaration was a shared silence full of meaning.

And so, although it was not the one for which they had been praying, Jonathan's family got a miracle giving them comfort and closure. Jonathan was not cured in the medical sense of the word. He did not get to go home with Mom and Dad, partake of Aunt Mazie's prizewinning pecan pie, and learn to ride a bike. He never was able to go fishing on the pond in the old rowboat with Uncle Jake and Cousin Lucas as his family had hoped. Inexplicably, however, he was privileged to come back from the dead to say one last good-bye to his family, and to receive the proper last rites of love, which would have been denied to him with an initial sudden passing. The bizarre circumstances of Jonathan's death rendered him even more special in his family's eyes. The extended W clan viewed Jonathan's brief resurrection as truly miraculous.

And who is to say it wasn't?

1. The fetus normally swallows amniotic fluid. Prenatal blockage of the fetal bowel may prevent proper swallowing of amniotic fluid. Since the fetus is not absorbing the fluid, it accumulates in the uterus. A fetus with intestinal blockage will need surgery shortly after birth to relieve the obstruction and permit normal eating and elimination. Occasionally congenital intestinal blockage is associated with serious syndromes, including those in which the fetus has an extra chromosome, such as *Down syndrome*. In the absence of an anatomic obstruction, polyhydramnios may indicate a compromised or brain-damaged fetus with poor swallowing function.

2. This severe defect develops by the fifth or sixth week of pregnancy. The embryo's forebrain fails to divide into right and left cerebral hemispheres, resulting in midline brain and facial defects. Holoprosencephaly is rare, occurring in one of its variations in only one out of sixteen thousand births. Its most severe form is Cyclops, a baby with a single nonfunctioning rudimentary eye in the middle of its forehead, and a proboscis instead of a nose. Cyclops malformation is lethal within minutes to hours.

3. S. J. Dudrick, D. W. Wilmore, H. M. Vars, et al., *Surgery* 64(1) (July 1968): 134–42.

4. Elisabeth Kübler-Ross, *On Death and Dying* (New York: Simon and Schuster/Touchstone, 1969).

3

Motorcycle Boy

Trying to Die

"His heart rate is falling again!" Heather, Jake's nurse for the morning shift, quickly moved into action. In what might look to a bystander as one swift motion she disconnected Jake's breathing tube from his ventilator, grabbed a resuscitation bag, and began to ventilate him at the rapid rate of sixty to eighty breaths per minute. Numbers that indicated his heart rate flashed on the monitor screen mounted above his warmer bed. The gathering crowd of neonatal nurses, doctors, and respiratory therapists watched expectantly as the blips on the screen appeared closer together, reflecting the baby's slowly rising heart rate: 50 . . . 60 . . . 68 . . . 77 . . . 92 . . . 118 . . . 135 . . . 150. Simultaneously Jake's color improved, turning from deep purple-blue to pink. Once again Jake had tried to die. Once again our NICU staff had foiled that very best effort to date.

Jake had just recovered from *bradycardia*, neonatal jargon for the phenomenon in which a baby's heart rate plummets to dangerously low levels. Like many words in medicine, bradycardia is derived from Greek: *brady* meaning *slow*, and *cardia* having its root in the word for *heart*. Jake staged this bradycardia prank often, sometimes several times a day, usually for no apparent reason. At least the doctors and nurses caring for

33

him could not figure out why he kept doing this. Ordinarily bradycardia follows *apnea*, a cessation of breathing for at least twenty seconds. When a neonate doesn't breathe, the oxygen level in his blood goes down. The ensuing lack of oxygen causes the falling heart rate. This is a paradoxical response; outside the neonatal period, low oxygen levels cause a rapid heart rate. But Jake's breathing efforts were being supported by a ventilator every two seconds, so he could not be apneic for as long as twenty seconds. A cardiac workup had revealed no intrinsic heart problem that might have accounted for these episodes. They were unrelated to his feedings as well, so we didn't think the bradycardia was from *gastroesophageal reflux*, a common cause of bradycardia in preterm infants.

Jake M had been born six weeks before his due date to a thirty-five-year-old first-time mother. Jake's father, Mrs. M's husband, was reputed to be a British banker employed by a French bank somewhere in Germany. At least that was what the note from Zelda our social worker said. We never actually saw Mr. M, not even once during his son's five-month hospitalization. Jake's parents later divorced, Mrs. M remarried, and her new husband adopted Jake. Many years after Jake's admission, I found out that in fact there was a story there, a very intriguing one, one from which soap operas are made. Mrs. M, now Mrs. B, told me herself. If you must know the details, you'll have to ask her about it. My lips are sealed.

Because of the early delivery, Jake suffered from lack of pulmonary *surfactant*, the phospholipid layer meant to prevent lungs from collapsing on exhalation. He had *hyaline membrane disease (HMD)*, the illness caused by lack of surfactant that affects preterm infants' lungs. These were the pre-artificial surfactant days. Treatment for Jake did not include today's magic of animal-derived surfactant administered directly into his lungs. Had he been born seven years later, he would have received that kind of artificial surfactant. With the benefit of surfactant he might have required a ventilator for two or three days at the most, instead of three months. His hospitalization of five months would have been cut to about five weeks.

Instead, by two months of age Jake was stuck on his ventilator. All attempts to decrease the rate or inflating pressure supporting his lungs failed. When he accidentally *extubated*—pulled out his own breathing tube—he decompensated rapidly. Therefore Jake was unlikely to wean off the ventilator anytime soon.

Unfortunately for Jake he was the quintessential "WWM"—a "wimpy white male"—a well-known nickname for babies such as Jake. "Wimpy white male" is another of the medical shorthand nonscientific terms that we doctors find descriptive. Almost any serious or life-threatening condition at birth, with the notable exceptions of congenitally dislocated hips, congenital hypothyroidism, and Edward's syndrome *(Trisomy 18)* are more common in male infants.[1] Multiple statistical analyses have demonstrated that white male babies have a higher incidence of HMD than white female babies. For reasons that we also don't know, perhaps related to the presence of the smaller Y chromosome, or to the lack of that second larger X chromosome with which girl babies are endowed, or lower estrogen levels, male infants exhibit higher mortality rates than female infants. The origin of "wimpy white male" is unknown. It's possible that WWM originated during the 1960's, when the women's liberation movement began. A tour through any NICU reveals that the preponderance of large, slightly preterm babies requiring assisted ventilation is male, with a disproportionate number being Caucasian.

Parents sometimes don't share our sense of humor regarding medical shorthand. Once I used the term on teaching rounds to describe a seven-pound slightly preterm male infant with significant HMD. The mother of the particular WWM about whom I was talking was seated at her son's bedside. Less than pleased with my "medical" introduction of her son to the pediatric residents, WWM's mother interrupted our rounds to tell me that she didn't appreciate my referring to her baby that way. Actually she was quite blunt: "Doctor, don't use that term when you talk about Henry. I'm tired of hearing it. It's ugly. It's making fun of him, and I don't find it funny. Not at all!"

I apologized to Henry's mother, and for the sake of political correctness, I have promised myself not to use the term WWM, at least not when parents are in earshot. And I never use the term if an infant is in danger of dying.

An Offer He Can't Refuse

From day one Jake's HMD was very severe. His condition required dangerously high pressures and rapid rates on the ventilator to keep him alive. We suspected but could not prove that he was also infected with a bacterial infection known as *Group B Streptococcus (GBS)*, the technical name of which is *streptococcus algalactia.* GBS is the most common bacterial infection seen at birth, and has been for the last thirty years when it replaced *Staphylococcus aureus* as infectious disease public enemy number one in newborns.[2] GBS makes infants very ill with pneumonia, generalized infection, and sometimes meningitis. The toxins released from the organisms cause profound drops in blood pressure and circulatory collapse. Mortality approaches fifty percent in affected premature infants.

The actual incidence of neonatal GBS infection has declined markedly over the last few years since near universal adoption of a protocol for its prevention.[3] In Jake's case, the combination of immature lungs, probable infection, and the accompanying inflammation made it even harder to provide him with adequate oxygen.

Early in Jake's course of treatment the combination of surfactant deficiency and high-inflating pressures predisposed his lungs to develop rupture of his *alveoli,* the tiny air sacs in his lungs where the real action of gas exchange takes place. When alveoli rupture, the baby develops a *pneumothorax:* a collapsed lung in layman's terms. Lung collapse is actually the result of the *pneumothorax.* Air accumulates in the potential space between the lung and the chest wall, a space where normally only a tiny bit of fluid is found, and certainly no air. With each ventilator breath more air is pumped into this space. This tiny potential space rapidly becomes a real, ever-expanding space. This phenomenon is called a tension *pneumothorax.* The tension or pressure from this forced-in air causes the lung on the same side to collapse. Air exchange in the collapsed lung is severely compromised. Large tension pneumothoraces also compress the lung on the opposite side as well, further encroaching on air exchange. The pressure buildup of air in the chest impairs blood return to the heart.[4] The heart, like any engine, cannot run on empty, and so cannot pump blood to the lungs or to the body. The baby becomes very

36

blue *(cyanotic),* and the blood pressure drops suddenly. In tiny babies the increased pressure in the chest prevents blood flow from the large veins draining the structures of the head from returning to the heart. Backup of blood may cause hemorrhage into the fragile preterm brain, resulting in an *intraventricular hemorrhage (IVH).* Unless the pressure within the chest is relieved quickly and circulation and oxygenation restored, death frequently follows the development of a large tension pneumothorax.

Over the course of the first eight days of his life, Jake tested fate and the skill of his doctors by developing five air leaks or pneumothoraces, five different times. Each time he developed one, he nearly died. The fifth pneumothorax on the eighth day of his life was the worst. The tension pneumothorax was accompanied by a rare and deadly *pneumopericardium,* a collection of air in the membranous sac that surrounds the heart. The air around the heart restricts its expansion. The heart cannot fill with blood and its pumping action is severely impaired. Without prompt evacuation of the air surrounding the heart, the patient dies. NICU nurses patiently ventilated Jake with an *ambu bag* for twenty-two long minutes as I struggled to remove the air through an *intravenous* catheter I had inserted just below his sternum into the pericardial space. I worked as quickly as I could to suck out the air as it accumulated while we waited for the arrival of a surgeon who would make a small incision at the base of the breastbone, cut into the sac surrounding the heart, and place a more effective drainage tube.

Each time we suspected a pneumothorax, or saw one on his chest X ray, we stuck a needle into Jake's chest between his ribs a little below his clavicle to the left or right of his sternum to rapidly remove the air. Then we placed a large plastic tube into his chest laterally between his ribs on the same side to drain the air on a continuous basis. The chest tube was hooked up to a vacuum seal and suction. The hole in the lung sealed over after three to five days, and the tube was then removed. Sometimes we had to place the tubes in the front of the chest, in the same place we had stuck our small needle to aspirate air. For cosmetic reasons we tried to avoid that placement. Today's smaller more flexible chest tubes are frequently not even sewn to the skin, and they leave little or no scar. The old ones, such as the ones I used on Jake, required suturing and often left ugly scars.

Most days during Jake's first week of life, he was the sickest baby in the unit. Mrs. M, having her first baby at age thirty-five, took all of Jake's problems in stride. Generally speaking my experience has been that elderly *primigravidas* (by definition, women over thirty-five having their first baby) are nervous Nellies, demanding perfection in the treatment of their offspring. Often they have delayed child bearing to finish their education or to establish a career. Generally they are well educated and may even have been on fertility drugs or have undergone in-vitro fertilization. One can almost hear their biological clocks ticking as they wonder if their sick infant will survive. *Tick-tock. This is my last chance, doctor. Tick-tock. You better make sure he survives and is normal, or else. Tick-tock.* I read, or perhaps over-read, this message in their eyes, their spouses' eyes, and in the grandparents' eyes.

Well read in medical matters, often courtesy of the Internet, these older mothers view medicine solely as a science. As one hires a carpenter, instructs him on the job to be done, and pays the bill when the result is satisfactory, so older parents sometimes behave this way toward the neonatal staff, both nurses and doctors. The contribution of the baby himself, genetic variability, natural variation, and the role of the unknown are discounted. One hundred percent is the only passing grade for the doctor and hospital. The art of medicine is not acknowledged, let alone valued. In contrast, even our new mantra *evidenced-based medicine*—accumulate all the data and come to a conclusion as to the best treatment—doesn't insist on one hundred percent. If treatment A is successful seventy percent of the time, and treatment B is successful only forty percent of the time, it is a no-brainer that we should use treatment A. But that means that thirty percent of the babies who get treatment A won't respond positively. Was it the wrong treatment? Perhaps for that particular baby, but the scientific statistical evidence favors treatment A.

But Mrs. M wasn't like that. Although some mornings she asked endless questions, they were pertinent and not repetitious. The staff did not view her as threatening or "high maintenance," another unflattering medical jargon term for a parent who takes up—in the view of the nurses or doctors—too much time for questions, reassurance, or updates, especially when the infant is doing well and his or her condition hasn't changed in the last twenty-four to forty-eight hours. We physicians think we are busy all the time. Not to our credit, we often approach parental education regarding an infant's condition in the same manner we received education in college: Here's the information; I gave you the lecture, now you should learn; I shouldn't have to repeat myself; I'm not going to spoon-feed you. But it doesn't always work that way for many families. Parents of sick babies often hear only the first sentence of bad news or complicated explanations. The rest of the explanation might as well be in a foreign language. "Med-speak" refers to the jargon doctors use, sometimes forgetting that the patient doesn't understand. Organized medicine somehow has to develop a better way to inform parents through an interactive method that progresses at the individual's own level and pace, making each parent feel a part of their baby's care, without tying up excessive amounts of medical staff's time.

Jake's mother was convinced that Jake would not only survive, but would be normal—as normal as he would have been without the NICU stay and its complications. She spent hours daily in the unit, talking to her son, reading *Green Eggs and Ham* to him, and gossiping with the nurses. She swore that Jake's eyes turned toward her as she approached his bed and said, "Hey Jake, how's it going today?"

Still, by three weeks of life, Jake had become a chronically ill baby. He was on a relatively high level of support on the ventilator, and he still required high concentrations of oxygen. He was subject to repeated bouts of pneumonia. His favorite trick was to drop his heart rate into the fifties, and to take his merry time recovering. One day he pulled this stunt on my watch. I went over to the bedside, and while the nurses were resuscitating him I drew close to his bed.

Assuming this episode was under his control—which it obviously was not, how could it have been?—I whispered into his ear, "Jake, if you don't stop doing this, you won't get a motorcycle for your sixteenth birthday."

Jake's heart rate immediately rose to normal levels.

We were all surprised, and since Jake was once again okay, we had a good laugh out of it. We even told Mrs. M, and she was amused as well. Thank God the woman had a sense of humor. To be sure, most parents would not have found this funny. The response of the average anxious parent might well have been: My baby almost died, and you told him he can't have a motorcycle? What kind of nutcase professional are you? How can you joke at a critical time like this?

But Mrs. M was not the average parent. She took each of Jake's problems in stride. In her mind her baby was not only going to survive, but he was going to be normal. She believed that Jake would excel at sports and go to college. Whatever it would take to get him there was alright with her. Ventilators, chest tubes, blood transfusions, threats to withhold a motorcycle, it didn't matter as long as the outcome would be a good one. And she was confident that the ultimate outcome would be just that.

Although in the heat of the moment Jake appeared to have taken my threat to heart, he continued to behave like any other little boy to a challenge to his behavior. I'll try it again. And again. And again. Each time, in addition to resuscitation with additional oxygen and ventilation, I repeated my threat: Okay Jake, here's the scoop. If you continue to have bradycardia, there will be no motorcycle for your sixteenth birthday.

Perhaps my timing was impeccable. Perhaps I had subconsciously waited for the turning point during each episode. Perhaps he recognized and responded to the sound of my voice. Perhaps we only wanted to believe in the magic of the incantation. Whatever the case, each time I used the motorcycle ploy Jake's heart rate recovered rapidly. His overall condition, however, remained critical.

Denouement

The lowest point of Jake's hospitalization for Mrs. M was the day the doctors decided that Jake would not come off of the ventilator for months, and that our unanimous consensus was that he needed a *tracheostomy*. Once a premature infant approaches his due date and both the weaning off of the ventilator appears unlikely and discharge home on a ventilator is in the not-too-distant future, it is best to remove the *endotracheal tube,* which enters the trachea via the nose or mouth, and replace it with a tube placed directly in the trachea. The ventilator attaches directly to the tracheostomy tube. It's a more secure airway. If it comes out, with some practice (which parents get before discharge) the parents can replace it. Endotracheal tubes require considerable expertise to place, expertise that a parent cannot hope to attain. Most pediatric residents never acquire this skill since they have so few babies on which to attempt intubation. In addition, a baby with an endotracheal tube cannot suck on a bottle, and may lose his suck reflex. Worse, he may develop an oral aversion that makes subsequent feeding a nightmare rather than a pleasant bonding experience between parent and child.

Normally calm, Mrs. M lost her equanimity when confronted with the possibility of a tracheostomy. To her, a tracheostomy meant permanent disability. But Jake was requiring close to one hundred percent oxygen again. He had failed to improve with his latest course of steroids. Tracheostomy appeared to be inevitable, and the sooner the better. Uncharacteristically distraught, Mrs. M requested a day to think about the surgery. Overnight, Jake weaned to fifty percent oxygen and a lower rate on his ventilator. Mrs. M had gone to the beach and spent the night praying in her favorite spot by the ocean. She had concluded that if Jake was not better, she would sign for the surgery. But the following morning the surgery was no longer needed. Perhaps Mrs. M's prayers worked.

Thanks to steroids, by Jake's five-month birthday he was off the ventilator. In those days we used steroids freely and in relatively high doses. The only side effects that we acknowledged were short term and treatable: stomach irritation, high blood pressure, high blood sugar, and susceptibility to infection. We later learned, through *meta-analysis* of many published studies, that steroids can profoundly affect growth in general, and brain growth in particular. Follow-up studies showed decreased head growth (reflecting decreased brain growth) and/or an increased chance of development of *cerebral palsy* in babies treated with steroids versus equally sick infants who did not receive steroids. When we treated Jake with steroids, we didn't worry about the long-term outcome as much as the short-term outcome—get him off the ventilator so he wouldn't die of end-stage lung disease

Despite the steroids, Jake's lungs were badly scarred by the ventilator and he still required some additional oxygen at five months of age. This need for supplemental oxygen was the only obstacle standing in the way of hospital discharge. Every time we tried to withdraw the small additional amount of oxygen he seemed to require, he turned blue, breathed too fast, or didn't finish his bottle feeds. Clearly he needed the additional oxygen. We just could not wean him off this small amount. Jake was eating well with no need for tube feedings and was gaining weight at a normal rate, so he met all the other criteria for discharge. Although our NICU had not yet sent home a baby requiring oxygen, Jake seemed the ideal candidate. His mother was quite capable of home management of his medical needs, including oxygen. And, furthermore, she was committed to doing it correctly. We arranged for home oxygen and an apnea monitor. On the day of his discharge from the unit, we had a little cake in his honor.

After Jake's discharge his mother made it her personal mission to appear publicly on TV in local ads for the Red Cross. She encouraged blood donation, telling the local community of the essential role that blood transfusion had in saving her baby's life. Our neonatal unit nurses' relationships with Jake and Mrs. M did not end with discharge. Several NICU nurses baby-sat—for free—to allow Mrs. M time for errands and appointments. She was a single mother with only an elderly mother to help her care for a child with complex medical needs. Dad the banker was still in Europe and out of the domestic picture.

Jake and Mrs. M were frequent visitors to the neonatal unit. Mrs. M carried Jake's portable oxygen tank on her back in a sling. She faithfully brought Jake back for periodic follow-up appointments to the developmental clinic. Despite the steroids and grim studies to the contrary, Jake did surprisingly well in his physical growth and neurological development. Other than signs of a very mild form of cerebral palsy, one that solely affected his gait (his heel cords were tight and he tended to toe-walk), he was basically a healthy child. When he was four years old, we graduated him from the developmental clinic with an almost normal exam. His prognosis for a successful life as a normal child and productive adult was excellent. Jake received an official graduation diploma with a teddy bear seal signed by the attending neonatologist and the clinic nurse.

Jake and Mrs. M initially attended all our Valentine's Day neonatal reunions. When Jake reached the age when he couldn't miss school to attend, we saw him less frequently. Every so often I received a card or note from Mrs. M with an update and a picture of Jake. Jake's Aunt Lauryl worked at the hospital, so from time to time I received additional updates in the hallway. By all accounts Jake was thriving.

Our city is located on the east coast. From June 1 through November 30 we are subject to hurricane warnings, watches, and occasional evacuations. The last direct hit was David in 1979. David was a category II storm and caused millions of dollars of damage to homes, businesses, and beaches. Some neighborhoods remained without electricity for weeks. We take our hurricanes seriously, especially at the hospital. While most of our recent hospital construction will withstand a category II or maybe even a category III storm, the NICU is built out over an old roof and will not withstand even a category II direct hit. When a hurricane threatens we evacuate all of our sick babies to inland NICUs, and leave only one doctor in house for the duration of the evacuation. The rest of us hightail it out of town, but return as soon as all is clear. The busiest time is the twenty-four to forty-eight-hour period after the danger has passed. Then all the patients are shipped back to us. All hands are needed to readmit our charges.

In 1999, during the evacuation for Hurricane Floyd (which would turn out to miss us completely), I stopped on the way back to town at a Cracker Barrel restaurant for lunch with my husband, my elderly parents, and our graying black Lab. Actually Ladydog took her lunch in the parking lot next to the car.

"Hey, Dr. Sacks!"

When I heard my name called, I looked around the small gift shop omnipresent in every Cracker Barrel restaurant from one end of the country to the other. Lots of my friends were also on their way back to town, but they wouldn't call me "Dr. Sacks." I expected to see one of our NICU nurses. Instead, to my surprise, I saw Mrs. M headed toward me. She and her family were also returning to town after the evacuation.

Jake's mother continued to yell across the room. "Hey, Jake, come on over here to see Dr. Sacks and show her."

Show me what? I had no idea what Jake had that I must see right now. Jake walked over, and without further maternal prompting pulled up his tee shirt! At first I was taken aback by this display of teenage flesh, but then I noted two small fresh scars on the left and right sides of his chest in the front. Jake's chest tube scars had been repaired! Evidently they had been so ugly that he felt self-conscious about them as he moved through adolescence. They were a blow to his teenage ego. A plastic surgeon had improved their appearance in an office procedure. Jake and his mother were not angry with me or any of the other doctors about the need for further surgery. They weren't trying to embarrass me. They simply wanted to show me the good results that had been achieved.

Jake grew up keenly aware of his shaky start in life and of the pivotal role that the doctors and nurses of Pine Grove Hospital played in saving him. His mother and stepfather made sure of that, and made sure that he understood the role of the Divine in his full recovery.

As a teenager, Jake volunteered for two years at our local Ronald McDonald House, serving on the teen board, and by his words and very existence, giving encouragement to the parents who stay there to be close to their sick infants. His high school created a project, called a "rock-a-thon," by which they raised money for charity by rocking for hours on end in rocking chairs. The year he was in charge of this project, the money was donated to our NICU. We purchased two rocking chairs for parents to use to comfort their infants during the babies' convalescence.

When Jake turned sixteen, I sent him a special gift for his special birthday—a motorcycle, a six-inch-by-two-inch Limoges porcelain Harley Davidson.

"This is the closest I suspect your mom will ever let you get to a motorcycle" the accompanying card stated. Knowing Jake's mother, I bet she and Jake had a good laugh.

Jake graduated from college in May 2007. Although he had previously expressed an interest in the ministry, he chose to major in journalism. Soon he was gainfully employed as a reporter for a small newspaper in South Carolina.

I last saw Jake several months after his college graduation. He showed up at the hospital on a Saturday night with a mission to accomplish. His good friend from college had given birth to a premature infant. The ophthalmologist who examined the baby, Charles, for signs of *retinopathy of prematurity* found a potentially vision-threatening problem involving the baby's optic nerves. Jake accompanied Charles's mother, who was worried and confused. A doctor had already spoken to her husband, but he did not understand what the doctor said, so he couldn't convey the information to his wife. She hoped to get the on-call doctor to explain the findings in terms she could understand. As luck (Jake thought it was not luck, but Divine coincidence) would have it, I was the on-call doctor that Saturday night! Although I had never formally made rounds on Charles before, I looked in the chart for the ophthalmologist's notes. I spent twenty minutes with the baby's mother and Jake doing the best I could to explain the uncertainty of Charles's condition. Then Jake asked me if I would pray with them. That was a first for me. The three of us joined hands in the anteroom of the special-care nursery. Jake offered a simple but meaningful prayer: "We thank you, God, for the gift of Charles's life. We hope and pray that You will be with Charles and his parents throughout this hospitalization, and that he will come home safely to them. We pray that You grant Charles useful vision. Give us Your Divine help. Guide his parents to acceptance of whatever outcome is destined for Charles. We pray that You grant them the courage to deal with Charles's future. Amen."

I would wish for every colleague of mine the encouragement of such a follow-up visit with a former patient.

Sadly, two years later Jake was involved in an automobile accident and was killed instantly. He was the passenger, and it was a freak, no-fault accident. His tragic demise, years after thwarting death as a neonate, reminds us of both the blessing and the fragility of life. Jake's college graduation picture still rests under the glass top of my desk, and I still hear his words about the courage needed to press on in the face of disaster.

1. The preponderance of female over male neonates with Trisomy 18 is easily explained. A fertilized egg with three instead of two number 18 chromosomes gives rise to an infant with lethal anomalies involving the heart, brain, kidneys, and/or bowel. Ninety percent of live born babies with Trisomy 18 die within the first year of life. Many afflicted fetuses are lost prior to birth through spontaneous early miscarriage or stillbirth. The preponderance of spontaneous pregnancy losses with Trisomy 18 are male, implying that male fetuses with Trisomy 18 are too weak to survive even in utero. Female fetuses, even with the anomaly, are stronger and more frequently survive to term.

2. GBS colonizes the vaginal tract of one third of pregnant women of all races and all socioeconomic and educational levels. It is an equal opportunity pathogen. Mothers occasionally develop a bladder infection with this organism, but most often carriers of GBS are totally asymptomatic. Despite the lack of apparent problems, colonized mothers can pass on the infection to their fetus/baby during labor and delivery, especially if membranes are ruptured for more than twelve hours.

3. Committee on Infectious Diseases and Committee on Fetus and Newborn, American Academy of Pediatrics, "Revised Guidelines for Prevention of Early-onset Group B Streptococcal (GBS) Infection," *Pediatrics* 99 (3) (1997): 489–96.

4. Blood flow via the superior and inferior vena cava, the large blood vessels returning blood for the head (superior) and the rest of the body (inferior) back to the heart is compromised. Blood follows the physical rules for all fluids—it flows downhill. When pressure inside the chest is high, blood tends to back up in the venous circulation, and doesn't reach its central destination, the heart.

4

THE LONG NIGHT

Early Advances in Neonatal Care

The late 1980's was a heady time for the specialty of neonatology. Advances in neonatal ventilator technology, combined with the widespread prenatal use of the potent steroid hormone *betamethasone*, had enabled the survival of increasing numbers of very tiny babies. Rashan J, a two-week-old African-American baby boy, who weighed a mere pound and a half at birth at twenty-six weeks gestation, was one such baby. Fortunately his mother had received two injections of prenatal steroids, so despite his low birth weight and extreme prematurity, Rashan's respiratory distress (HMD) was only moderately severe and amenable to treatment.

The prenatal steroid story is especially close to my heart. In my residency in 1974, during rotations through the neonatal unit at Sylvania University Hospital, each doctor in training had to prepare and present a paper to our pediatric peers. Late in my first year of training I chose to research the literature regarding the effect of prenatal steroids on neonatal lung disease. I reviewed all thirty of the papers published in English on that subject as of 1974. This task involved looking through the *Index Medicus* for published papers, finding the journals in the stacks in the hospital library, and then Xeroxing them myself. What journals the library didn't carry, the librarian requested for me through interlibrary loan. There was no *Pub-Med* to query, and no articles posted online. Online was where you waited to buy tickets for the movies. My presentation was well received, especially by Dr. Paterson, my attending, who subsequently arranged for me to give OB/GYN Grand Rounds on the topic. Either the topic itself, or the thrill of presenting Grand Rounds, or the excitement of working with the dynamic Dr. Paterson, or a combination of all of those factors, hooked me on neonatology from that point on.[1]

The story of discovery of the effect of prenatal administration of steroids is a fascinating tale of serendipity striking the prepared mind. In 1968 a New Zealand obstetrician, Dr. George Liggins, was studying the causes of preterm birth in the sheep model.[2] Liggins administered steroids to pregnant ewes with the designed goal of inducing preterm labor. As he planned, the ewes delivered their lambs prematurely. But Dr. Liggins astutely noticed that these particular preterm lambs didn't die within a few hours of birth from immature lungs as he had expected, based upon his previous research experience with premature lambs. On autopsy, these prenatally steroid-exposed premature lambs appeared to have structurally mature lungs! Their air sacs were not collapsed as he had expected, based on the lambs' degree of prematurity. A study in human subjects soon followed. In a randomized controlled double-blind study— the gold standard for research—Dr. Liggins administered two doses of betamethasone twenty-four hours apart, or two doses of placebo to mothers at risk for preterm delivery due to preterm labor or preeclampsia.[3] Dr. Liggins hoped to induce lung maturity in the infants subsequently born to the women in the experimental group. Since premature lung disease, or *hyaline membrane disease*, was the primary cause of death in premature babies under thirty-four weeks gestational age in the early 1970's, steroid-induced lung maturity had the potential to save many lives.

Translation of research from one animal species to another and ultimately to the human species is not always successful. What works in an animal model may not work in humans. Sheep and pigs are traditionally used for research on fetuses and the neonate, since most results in these species appear to be valid also in human subjects. Fortunately for the course of high-risk obstetrics, steroids had the identical effect on human fetuses as they had on preterm lambs. Babies born prematurely to mothers in the experimental betamethasone group had a much lower incidence of HMD, and consequently they also had a lower mortality rate than the infants in the control group. Short-term follow-up of the betamethasone group of infants indicated no adverse effects on general health, growth, or development. Liggins reported his findings in the *Journal of Pediatrics*.[4]

After publication of Liggins' landmark clinical study and other subsequent confirmatory studies,[5] a number of obstetricians began giving betamethasone to their patients in preterm labor and obtained the same good results. An unfortunate fact of medical life is that treatment consensus moves surprisingly slowly. That was especially the situation before the Internet. Of course a group of rapid adopters, physicians who read an article and immediately put that knowledge into practice, always existed. Most doctors, however, are cautious and are not rapid adopters. Therefore, in the 1980's, evidence for clinical improvement induced by a particular treatment reported in the medical literature didn't reach the patient as quickly as it should have. And unfortunately, sometimes it never reached the patient at all. It wasn't until 1994 that the National Institutes of Health produced a formal position paper stating unequivocally that steroid administration to women at risk of preterm delivery from twenty-four to thirty-four weeks gestation represented the best practice based on review and evaluation of all the evidence published since 1972.[6] It had taken twenty-two years for a relatively inexpensive treatment with practically no downside to travel from the pages of a medical journal to the bedsides of a majority of patients in need of such treatment.

My patient Rashan had responded to prenatal betamethasone just as described in the literature. Despite his extreme prematurity he had been weaned to low settings on a ventilator specifically designed for newborns. Since the days of my residency, ventilator technology had also progressed. During the ten to fifteen years since the first neonatal ventilators made their debut in the late 1960's, there had only been one way to ventilate babies. They were hooked up to a respirator that delivered either a set pressure designed to achieve adequate lung volume or a set volume delivered with whatever pressure it took to assure that that particular volume was delivered. Maximal rates on neonatal ventilators were sixty to eighty breaths per minute, similar to the fastest spontaneous respiratory rates babies can sustain long term. Much of the volume of each breath, or *tidal volume* as the medical profession terms it, is wasted. Inhaled[7] air first fills up the trachea, main stem bronchi, and smaller airway branches, which serve as conduits to the air sacs. This space is called physiologic dead space and no air exchange occurs in these areas. If one measures the tidal volume delivered, and subtracts from it the dead space, what is left is the volume of air theoretically available for air exchange. Tidal volume in neonates is very small, five to ten cubic centimeters per *kilogram*, or about two teaspoons per pound of body weight. In a micropreemie (infants less than one kilogram) tidal volume may be as little as one half teaspoon.

Conventional thinking about neonatal ventilation imploded in the early 1980's. The FDA gave its seal of approval to a totally novel ventilator, the *high frequency jet ventilator (HFJV)*. This amazing machine is capable of breathing for babies at rates measured not in breaths per minute, but in hertz. One hertz equals sixty breaths per minute. We generally set these jet machines for seven hertz—a rate of 420 breaths per minute! At rates this high, tidal volume is minuscule, reduced to a tiny fraction of the actual volume of the trachea alone. One would not expect such miniaturized volumes to provide adequate ventilation. One would think that the air would exchange only in the windpipe and therefore would not provide adequate oxygen or *carbon dioxide* exchange to support life. But that's not what happens.

When placed on a HFJV a baby's chest does not rise and fall as it does with normal breathing or with a conventional ventilator; instead, the chest appears to vibrate. Sometimes the whole baby seems to shake gently and rapidly. There are theories as to why HFJV works, including spike ventilation, molecular diffusion, gas entrainment, magic. For as yet definitively inexplicable reasons, babies with severe lung disease actually do well on this mode of ventilation.

In 1985 there were only thirteen articles in the neonatal literature about HFJV. By the year of Rashan's birth, that number had more than doubled. On the night described in the following pages, my hospital did not yet possess one of these special machines in its ventilator fleet. My partner had requested a HFJV in our capital budget in 1987, more than a year prior to Rashan's birth, but it had not been approved. We had no idea when that approval would come. The cost of each HFJV was $15,000 in the 1980's, at least twice as much as a conventional ventilator. Our capital budget for the nursery was limited. Budget bureaucrats believed that most babies could be sustained without such a device, and that incubators and *intravenous* pumps were more vital, less costly, and could help more infants.

Life or Death

We had been giving Rashan's parents upbeat reports daily: "We expect that Rashan will be ready to breathe entirely on his own soon, without the ventilator. Maybe he will continue to need additional oxygen, but the ventilator will be gone. That's great news isn't it?"

But it was not to be. On his sixteenth day of life, Rashan's condition progressively worsened. We had already responded to his deteriorating condition by giving him higher concentrations of oxygen and by turning up the rate and pressure on his ventilator. Then, about 8:00 that evening his condition took a nose dive. He became difficult to oxygenate and almost impossible to ventilate. His lungs were stiff. I performed what doctors call a *differential diagnosis* of his condition. I considered all the factors that might be reasons for his declining status: infection, anemia, secretions clogging his breathing tube, tube in the wrong position, collapsed lung, pulmonary hemorrhage, or cardiac problem. The cause was probably not infection: his white blood cell count was cold stone normal, not suggestive of a hospital acquired *(nosocomial)* bacterial or viral infection. He was mildly anemic; giving him a booster transfusion of red blood cells might help with oxygen delivery, but would not cure his underlying condition. Our respiratory therapists tried to suction secretions from his trachea, but obtained just a normal amount. The color of his sputum did not suggest infection or hemorrhage. Rashan's chest

X ray showed the beginnings of *bronchopulmonary dysplasia*, or chronic neonatal lung disease. But there was no accumulation of free air—a *pneumothorax* or collapsed lung—that could have been treated by evacuation of the offending air. His breathing tube was in perfect placement. His lungs were not collapsed. An *echocardiogram* of his heart did not show the reason for his decline. There was nothing specific to treat. There was no magic bullet, no instant panacea for his respiratory problem. Since we didn't know what was wrong, we couldn't medically address his deteriorating condition directly. We had to use the trial and error method.

At ten o'clock I ordered another blood-gas. The results were far worse than I had imagined. His pH was 6.8, a level of acidosis not compatible with life for more than a few hours. His *carbon dioxide* level (pCO2) had jumped from a chronically high but acceptable 60 *torr* (*mm Hg*) to a sky-high 110 torr. I reacted to the numbers by adjusting Rashan's ventilator, jacking up both the pressure and the rate again, a maneuver calculated to increase the amount of air exchanged per minute, the physiologic way of blowing off carbon dioxide. I knew, however, that I was working with a double-edged sword. If Rashan survived the night, the trauma inflicted by pounding his lungs might damage them to the point where he couldn't recover.

Manipulations of his ventilator parameters failed to improve his condition. Rashan's follow-up blood-gas two hours later was no better. Was there a plug in his *endotracheal tube* that we couldn't suction out? I pulled out his lifeline—his endotracheal tube—and placed a new one. No mucus plug hung onto the end of the old tube. We repeated a chest X ray to determine the placement of the new tube. The film showed his lungs were now overexpanded because of the increased pressures we were using, but otherwise unchanged. The situation was grim: if I couldn't produce a significant improvement in his condition, by morning the baby would die, I would have failed, and Rashan's two-week-long fight to survive would have been in vain.

A maxim I remembered from my pediatric residency is that no one should die without the benefit of steroids. Back then we used steroids for overwhelming infection or autoimmune disease. Steroids work on chronic lung disease as well, although it usually takes twenty-four to forty-eight hours to begin to see results, and Rashan needed help immediately. I ordered large doses to be given intravenously.

By midnight Rashan's condition was desperate. He required pure oxygen and incredibly high pressures and maximal ventilator rates. My ventilator manipulations placed him at risk for rupturing a lung. If he ruptured a lung, he might not survive the cure—placing a drainage tube in his chest. If I were Dr. Kildare, or if Rashan's life and my career were a weekly television show, I would have placed him on the jet ventilator. In prime time the jet would have worked and Rashan would have been snatched from the jaws of death just after the last commercial break, and before the closing credits. If I'd had a jet I would have given it a try, but I didn't have one and I couldn't transfer Rashan to another NICU that had one, since the closest unit with a HFJV was two and half hours away by ground transport. It was raining, so helicopter transport was out, and Rashan was so unstable that he would have died in a prolonged ambulance transport. Real life is far more challenging than television drama, with far fewer happy endings.

I had to call his parents at home with the sad news. They knew from previous calls that Rashan had taken a turn for the worse. I planned to suggest that they come in to hold him for what might be the last time. Dad answered the phone.

"Mr. J, this is Dr. Sacks calling about Rashan." Parents always think it's bad news, so if it isn't, I always quickly add, "Your baby's fine, I just need to discuss with you . . ." I didn't add that sentence.

"Rashan has gotten very ill, very quickly. We have tried everything possible to make him better. He's way up on his ventilator settings, he's on antibiotics, he's gotten a blood transfusion, but he hasn't responded to anything yet." *Yet* means hope. *Yet* means we haven't given up.

Dad was silent. I waited, hoping he would say something, anything to continue this conversion. I didn't know what to say next, except that Rashan was dying.

"He's gonna be okay, isn't he?" Mr. J's reply was not an unusual parental response to bad news. Sometimes it's a case of not understanding what the doctor has said. But Rashan's Dad was an intelligent man. I'm sure on an intellectual level he understood what I had said. Dr. Kübler-Ross would interpret this response as the first stage in the grief process: denial.[8] Above all else, parents seek reassurance that all will eventually be well. Reassurance was one thing I could not in good conscience offer that tonight. Hope, maybe, but not reassurance.

"No, he may not be okay." I was pretty blunt. "I'm concerned that if Rashan doesn't show improvement soon, there is a possibility he might die tonight." There, I said it. I was the witness, the judge, and the jury. The evidence was in, and that awful fact was my best judgment.

I pictured Rashan's Dad on the other end of the line. I'd met him several times. He was a social worker by profession, but he looked more like a linebacker, Rosie Greer's doppelgänger. He was a big man. I wondered if he were crying or just in a state of shock. Did he believe me? Was he angry with me? Did he think I was incompetent? These last three thoughts demonstrate the insecurity that afflicted me then and still does now when I've run out of treatments for my tiny patients. I suspect other physicians may feel differently.

"What should I do now? Should I come to the hospital?" The man's voice was cracking. He understood the gravity of the situation.

"Yes, you and your wife should come to the hospital now. Don't speed. Please, be safe." They lived about twenty minutes away. Parents want to be with their sick or dying baby; they deserve to be; they need to be. But what good would it do if they had an accident on the way to the hospital? The situation that night could have been worse. Some of our parents lived in rural areas, had no car, and relied on the kindness of neighbors to give them a lift back and forth whenever possible. Some lacked gas money for a sixty to two hundred mile round trip. Social services could arrange Medicaid-financed transportation, but this had to be done at least twenty-four hours in advance. That kind of service is of no help in an emergency situation. At least the J family had a car in working order and didn't live too far away from the hospital.

"I'll be there as soon as I can. My wife has to stay with our two-year-old son. We have no one we can call to sit with him at this hour."

I learned later that this was an incomplete truth. With some effort the parents could have located a sitter. The real reason that Rashan's mother didn't accompany her husband was profoundly private. A deeply religious woman, she refused to allow the possibility that the Angel of Death was hovering at Rashan's bedside. She chose to stay home to plead with the Almighty to spare the life of her child, a decision I found out years later.

"Okay, I will talk with you more when you get here. Please drive carefully." I hoped I might have better news for him when he arrived.

Dad hung up the phone. We found out later that he immediately picked the receiver up again and dialed the home number of BJ Monroe, our senior neonatal respiratory therapist. BJ, our NICU's Miss Congeniality, amateur psychologist, and social butterfly, had taken a real liking to Rashan. She had bonded not only with the baby but with his parents as well. At one point BJ had given Rashan a San Francisco 49ers gold-and-red warm-up jacket. It was huge, but Rashan fit nicely into the sleeve. Only his head, endotracheal tube, and one arm with an intravenous line stuck out. BJ lived closer to the hospital than the family, and I suspected that in her haste she exceeded posted speed limits. Because of Rashan's Dad's call, she arrived at the unit ten minutes before Rashan's Dad, and that gave me an unexpected chance to discuss with her all that we had done and to pick her brain for more ideas.

"Dr. Sacks, you've done everything I can think of. There's nothing more to try. Sure wish we had a jet ventilator."

"Me, too."

If BJ's respected opinion, based on the expertise of fifteen years as a neonatal respiratory therapist, told her there were no more ventilator tricks without a jet ventilator, then there were no more for sure.

Rashan's Dad arrived in the NICU dressed in a gray sweat suit. His eyes were moist from crying, and his demeanor defeatist and depressed. Unbelievably, his son had gone from "off the ventilator soon" to deathly ill in a few hours. It never fails to amaze me, to frighten and humble me, how fast a neonate's condition can deteriorate from stable to critical. The nurses had already set up a rocking chair by Rashan's bedside. While Mr. J got comfortable in the chair, they gently wrapped Rashan in several blankets so he would stay warm off the radiant warmer. Then they carefully moved and repositioned the ventilator tubing, his EKG leads, and IV tubing. Today he would have a *pulse oximeter,* a noninvasive device to measure the oxygen saturation in his blood, to move as well. It would be wound around his hand or foot. Those had not yet been invented in Rashan's time. We did have a device called a transcutaneous oxygen monitor. It measured the oxygen level in the capillary blood by heating up a tiny area of the skin to 102 degrees and measuring the partial pressure of oxygen across the blood-skin membrane. Although that technology was not very accurate, it did trend well, and could tell us whether the baby was getting better or worse. Even with careful rotation of the probe site, however, the device left little burns, similar to the telltale cigarette burns one observes on abused and battered children. NICU abuse. Unfortunately Rashan couldn't even use that device because of the fragility of his skin.

Sometimes, when a baby reaches the end of the therapeutic line, when nothing short of a miracle will save the baby's life, we suggest to parents that we not prolong the inevitable, that we not lengthen the dying process. We propose that the support machines and medications that are not helping the baby be removed or discontinued. We suggest that the baby be allowed to die in peace naturally, without the additional burden of our technology. But when the end appears suddenly and unexpectedly, as occurred in Rashan's case, we are reluctant to make that suggestion. We always hope that what changed acutely for the worse may be reversible, and just as quickly, especially when we are unsure as to the etiology of the decline.

Throughout that long night Mr. J rocked his baby. The giant man holding the tiny infant would have made a great photo-op were it not for the sad nature of the situation. Dad sang to him, kissed him, told Rashan how much he loved him, and how much his mother loved him too. He took only one bathroom break, during which BJ took over the rocking. Rashan remained critical but surprisingly stable. His heart rate didn't drift downward; his blood pressure did not deteriorate. We didn't interrupt the father-son bonding to obtain any lab tests. What would have been the point of disturbing the dying baby and his grieving father? At

6:30 A.M. Rashan's Dad needed to go home to bring his wife back to the hospital after dropping off the two-year-old at day care. Mrs. J needed to hold Rashan for one last time. Mom, too, needed to say her good-byes. After he left, I decided to get a blood-gas to see if there was even the slightest improvement. More likely we would find out how much closer to death Rashan had come. His nurse wrapped his tiny heel with a small disposable diaper soaked in warm water to increase the circulation to his heel. With a proper increase in blood flow, we could obtain an arterialized capillary sample. Phillip, the morning-shift respiratory therapist, drew the sample and disappeared into the respiratory work area to run it.

A few minutes later he called the unit and asked to talk with me. "Dr. Sacks, I think I need to repeat the blood-gas. It must have an air bubble in it." An air bubble falsely raises the oxygen level and lowers the carbon dioxide level. For a baby who is not doing well, it may make the gas look a lot better than it really is.

"Well, Phil, what are the results? Just tell me." I knew I was not treating Phil respectfully. I'd been awake all night, but my efforts did not appear to have cured Rashan. To suggest that I was not in a good mood was being kind. Dying babies affected me that way, and still do. And, as usual, my type-A personality had little tolerance for sloppy technique or lame excuses. I wanted my information, and I wanted it now.

"Almost normal, Dr. Sacks. His pH is 7.3 and his pCO2 is down to his usual 55 torr. He's fixed. That is, if you believe this gas." I wanted with all my heart to trust those results, but I had no basis on which to anchor my belief. It was probably an inaccurate sample, probably an air bubble just as Phil had suggested.

"Get an arterial sample. An arterial stick will be more accurate."

Ten minutes later we all knew the truth. The results were the same. Rashan was no longer dying.

I rushed to intercept the J family at home. I had to be careful when they answered, lest they think I was calling to tell them that Rashan's status had worsened, or even that he had passed away. I didn't want them to suffer even a few seconds of those terrible thoughts. Rashan's Dad answered the phone. I didn't wait beyond hello.

"Mr. J, this is Dr. Sacks. Rashan is so much better, I just had to call you." I blurted out the words as quickly as I could, hopefully giving him no time to think the worst. "I cannot explain why he improved. It was nothing that we did for him."

Rashan survived that night. Eight weeks later he was discharged in excellent condition, on no medications, and off of oxygen. The last time we formally evaluated him in the developmental clinic shortly before his fifth birthday, he appeared to be somewhat hyperactive, but was succeeding in a normal preschool program. He tested out average for age on our abbreviated standard Denver Developmental testing. His parents were quite pleased with his progress and thankful to the medical and nursing staff for all our efforts to save their baby that dreadful night five years before. Today Rashan is a high school graduate. He had to overcome a significant learning disability to earn his diploma. He holds down a full-time job, he and his older brother are good friends, and he has an active social life. BJ still sees Rashan from time to time.

The morning after that long night, the staff racked its collective brains for an explanation of Rashan's rescue. Some thought that the rocking motion and gentle jostling in his father's arms might have dislodged an airway plug that was beyond the reach of our suction catheters. Others thought that maybe he really had an infection even though all the evidence pointed in the other direction. Perhaps the antibiotic coverage we started might have helped him through that night's crisis. Maybe the steroids worked faster than the twenty-four-hour window we expected. Another respiratory therapist thought that it just took a tincture of time for the changes on the ventilator to kick in. In retrospect twenty years later, it appears that Rashan may have had an acute episode of *pulmonary hypertension,* which passed with comfort measures and sedation. We never did reach a satisfying scientific consensus on the exact mode of his healing.

I'll bet Rashan's mother knows the answer.

1. Or maybe there is a less noble explanation. When I entered college I had wanted to be a veterinarian. My pre-vet advisor talked me out of that career choice and steered me toward human medicine. I think he anticipated that I wouldn't be accepted into veterinary school. Women just

didn't do things like that in the mid-1960's. Why did I choose neonatology? Neonatology deals with patients who cannot communicate in words; so does veterinary medicine!

2. G. C. Liggins, "Premature Delivery of Foetal Lambs Infused with Glucocorticoids," *Journal of Endocrinology* 45 (1969): 515–23.

3. Patients in each arm of the study are designated randomly to be either in the treatment group or the placebo group. The doctors and nurses caring for the patients do not know which ones receive the experimental treatment and which ones do not. The patients (or parents) do not know either. Those who analyze the data do not know which group was the control and which was the experimental. Therefore, there is no observer bias in assignment to treatment, care, or analysis of the study's results.

4. G. C. Liggins and R. N. Howie, "A Controlled Trial of Antepartum Glucocorticoid Treatment for Prevention of the Respiratory Distress Syndrome in Premature Infants," *Pediatrics* 50, no. 4 (1972): 515–25.

5. A. N. Papageorgiou, M. F. Desgranges, M. Masson, E. Colle, R. Shatz, and M. M. Gelfand, "The Antenatal Use of Betamethasone in Prevention of Respiratory Distress Syndrome: A Controlled Double-blind Study," *Pediatrics* 63, no. 1 (1979): 73–9.

   M. F. Block, O. R. Kling, and W. M. Crosby, "Antenatal Glucocorticoid Therapy for the Prevention of Respiratory Distress Syndrome in the Premature Infant," *Journal of Obstetrics and Gynecology*, 50, no. 2 (1977): 186–90.

6. "Effect of Corticosteroids for Fetal Maturation on Perinatal Outcomes," *NIH Consensus Statement*, 12, no. 2 (Feb. 28–Mar. 2, 1994): 1–24.

7. Actually, in the case of the ventilator, it isn't inhaled, so much as forced in.

8. Elisabeth Kübler-Ross, *On Death and Dying* (New York: Simon and Schuster/Touchstone, 1969).

5

THE COWARDS WE ARE

Dreaded Diagnosis

"I don't think I did this baby any favors, Linda. It was an awful mess in there when I opened her up. Pre-op I thought maybe I'd find some discreet area of dead gut that I could remove. You probably thought the same thing when you called me. Instead, all I saw was dead and dying bowel, sick bowel, and an occasional area of normal bowel. It was all intertwined. Operating on her was a real challenge. I took out what was clearly dead and left everything else alone, even if it looked iffy. A lot of what I left in looks pretty bad." An exhausted Dr. David Bellman looked down at me and dropped his voice. "I'm really concerned that those iffy areas I left in will go on to die. But then again, maybe they won't. Frankly, I just don't know. I guess maybe I should have just closed her up, stopped her meds, and allowed nature to take its course. I really don't know if what I did was best for her. I hope we're not sorry later."

"So, what now?" I looked the pediatric surgeon right in the eye. Our patient, Jamala, was critically ill and unlikely to survive after her extensive bowel resection. As a neonatologist I was damn tired of picking up the pieces after another surgery with unanticipated poor outcome. In our neonatal unit neonatologists were the primary physicians for all patients, including those who had to have surgery. Surgeons were the consultants who operated, but we had to run the show outside of the operating room. We talked with parents daily, shouldering clinical responsibility 24/7. This collaborative approach usually worked to the advantage of the medical doctors, surgeons, and, most of all, the patients, but now the surgical mess would become my medical mess. It wasn't really Dr. Bellman's fault, but I would be the one left holding the bag.

"Maybe in a few days or a week, if she doesn't die, I'll go back in and take a second look," Bellman continued. "By then I'll be able to tell if she's got enough bowel left to be salvageable. You know, some of these kids are pretty resilient. She may surprise us." Fortunately for me, Bellman was clueless about my hostile thoughts toward his fix-'em-all-up-no-matter-what surgical professional credo regarding any baby like Jamala. "At least that's what we can hope. I'll check back tomorrow." With a sheepish smile he wished me no further problems throughout the rest of the night, and walked to where the family was waiting to report the results of surgery to them.

I felt just the tiniest bit sorry for him. He looked wiped out, almost defeated. I thought he was sorry he didn't just close the baby up without trying to save her. But he couldn't or wouldn't admit that, at least not to me. Surgeons rush in to save the situation, but Bellman couldn't. Surgeons hate to admit that their skills and scalpels can't fix every defect. Come to think of it, most of us, as physicians trying our best under terrible circumstances, hate to admit when we don't know what to do, or worse, that there might be nothing left to do.

Jamala's parents, Tasha B and her boyfriend Antoine C, paraded in just as we got their baby settled on the radiant warmer after her non-curative surgery. The two young parents were flying higher than they'd been a few hours earlier when they'd consented to their daughter's surgery. Both were addicted to crack cocaine. They also partook of other recreational drugs, smoked cigarettes, and drank excessively. At the time of her delivery, Tasha's urine drug screen was positive for cocaine, heroin, and marijuana. There might have been other illicit substances present, but we didn't test for them. The two tried to listen to Dr. Bellman's explanation of their baby's critical postoperative condition. The complex information had to be processed through the hazy filter of street drugs into brains that had stopped formal learning in the ninth grade. Dr. Bellman reviewed his plan to reevaluate with a "second look" in a week or so with them. I wasn't sure if they realized that "second look" meant another surgery.

Bellman was uncharacteristically blunt. He didn't hedge as was his usual modus operandi: "There is a real chance that your baby may not survive."

Did they really understand? Holding hands nervously, Tasha and Antoine sat at Jamala's bedside for another ten minutes. They picked at her bed linens and squirmed in their chairs. The pair examined the new tubes and lines that had been inserted into their child, but between the two of them they didn't ask even one question. They didn't talk to Jamala to reassure her, nor did they stroke her limbs soothingly. Then, without so much as a "we'll be back in the morning" or "call us if there's any change in Jamala's condition," they vanished.

We didn't know it at the time, but for all intents and purposes the couple would abandon their infant. Over the next few weeks they resurfaced from time to time, usually high on cocaine, sometimes stoned, occasionally drunk. Once in a while they resembled the other NICU parents: appropriately concerned, with worried looks on their faces, anxious for the latest word on their baby's condition, grasping at any shred of hope. But for the most part, their behavior at Jamala's bedside was disinterested or inappropriate.

Based on her birth weight of four pounds and mild degree of prematurity at thirty-three weeks, from a medical standpoint Jamala should have done extremely well. Twenty-year-old Tasha had had no prenatal care. She'd presented in active labor to our emergency department. Hospital protocol called for the drug testing of urine of mothers with no prenatal care because the incidence of street drug use in pregnant women who don't seek prenatal care is many times higher than in women who do obtain prenatal care. Our toxicology lab reported the presence of multiple street drugs in Tasha's urine. My colleague Dr. Naomi Trent, who admitted Jamala, had already alerted social services about the high-risk social situation. Marianna, the social worker designated for our area, planned to talk with the couple. By law it was mandated that the case be turned over to child welfare services, known in Georgia as DFCS (pronounced "dē'•faks"), the Department of Family and Children's Services. After review of the case, discussions with the mother, and a home visit, the agency would make a written report and a recommendation for or against foster placement.

Despite Tasha's less-than-perfect pregnancy, Jamala started out well: good Apgar scores, minimal transient respiratory distress, a normal weight for her shortened gestation. Fortunately the heroin and the cocaine that Tasha had taken during pregnancy were not sufficient to stunt her baby's growth. The baby's urine, however, tested positive for drugs because of passive addiction, courtesy of her mother. Although we know that breast milk is best for all infants, especially preemies, we are reluctant to encourage mothers with substance abuse issues to breastfeed unless they are drug-free and in an active treatment program. The chance of transmitting drugs, especially cocaine, through mother's milk is high and unacceptable. We also don't know what other drugs an addicted mother might be using. The risks of an addicted mother's own breast milk clearly outweigh any benefits. In Jamala's case, however, the point was moot. Tasha wasn't interested in breastfeeding or in rehabilitation, so Jamala received commercially available formula specifically designed for premature babies.

Jamala fed poorly by bottle on account of her prematurity. Protocol called for supplementing her with tube feedings, which she tolerated for a week. Each time her nurse pulled back on her feeding tube to check for undigested formula prior to giving her the next feeding, they found none. Jamala's gut appeared to be functioning quite well.

At five in the morning on Jamala's ninth day of life, my beeper went off, waking me up at home out of a deep sleep. The number on the beeper display was that of our intermediate care nursery. I knew there could be trouble; intermediate didn't usually have any issues that warranted a middle of the night (or early, early morning) call. I got up, put on my robe, and went to the kitchen to call back. I didn't want to wake my husband, who had learned to sleep through the beeper noise, but not through phone calls.

"This is Dr. Sacks. Someone paged me."

"Dr. Sacks, this is Diane. I'm in the Intermediate Nursery taking care of the B baby tonight. She seems to be tolerating her feedings. I mean, well, there's no vomiting, but I noticed that her belly is very distended. I took care of her yesterday morning also, and it sure didn't look like this."

"Hold her feedings for now. I'll be there as soon as I can to evaluate her. I just need to get dressed." Without traffic my trip to the hospital took only eight minutes.

Doctors in the neonatal area (as do most doctors if they would only admit it) rely heavily on bedside nurses to be our eyes and ears. Depending on the length of the nursing shift and severity of patients' illnesses, neonatal nurses spend eight to twelve hours with their one to four tiny patients. In contrast, doctors may devote ten to thirty minutes on rounds to each patient once a day, and one to two minutes on sign-out rounds. Of course a critically ill baby often requires the constant presence of a physician at the bedside, sometimes for hours at a time. Jamala had been stable since birth. I doubted that any of my colleagues had spent more than fifteen minutes a day on morning rounds with her. I knew I certainly hadn't. During that short time on morning rounds, the doctor acquires a brief Polaroid picture of the baby, a static image in time. Perusing the nurses' notes from previous shifts, looking at lab results, and questioning the current bedside nurse add more information to the overall report. After examining the patient, evaluating all the other information, including any laboratory results or X rays, the doctor writes her note and goes on to the next patient. The bedside nurse would note any substantive change in the baby's condition during the day or night. The doctor does not stop by again until the next morning unless the nurse or parent voices concern, or if there is an issue that needs further investigation or immediate follow-up, or a true emergency occurs.

As an attending in the old precomputer and preelectronic medical records days—and Jamala was born in those old days—I strongly advised residents and medical students before morning rounds, "If you want to know what happened to your patient last night, read the nurse's notes. It's all there." And it was all there, sometimes in great detail. Today, for the most part, nurses chart by exception, using a checklist. I believe this documentation frenzy is driven by the fear of litigation. We teach our residents and nursing *orientees* that if a treatment isn't documented, it wasn't done. Of course a treatment might have been done; we just can't prove it to the twelve men and women deciding our professional fate in a malpractice case. Therefore, today one finds a colorful and informative nursing narrative only for the most significant or unexpected events. The rest of the documentation comprises yes or no checks on a list, or if called for, a number filling in a blank.

I arrived in the nursery and went immediately to Jamala's bedside. The small preemie's belly was grotesquely swollen. As I examined her, Jamala threw up a large quantity of yellow-green fluid, and simultaneously passed a stool that was mostly blood. Neither action had good portent. Her abdomen was also tender. Although I tried my best to be gentle, she winced as I examined her. A quick *differential diagnosis* formed in my brain: reflux, obstruction, formula intolerance, *ileus, necrotizing enterocolitis.*

Gastroesophageal reflux is a common neonatal problem. The junction between the esophagus and the stomach isn't tight in a preterm infant. In addition, it is forced to remain open when a feeding tube is left in place. Sometimes partially digested formula backs up, and the infant spits it out. On occasion, the fluid may even be slightly bile stained. But the abdomen in reflux isn't tender. I saw the fluid Jamala vomited. It didn't look like reflux to me. And reflux doesn't cause bleeding in the stool. Reflux wasn't her problem that night.

A congenital intestinal obstruction was very unlikely. The baby was already a week old and had passed many stools. Could she have an acquired obstruction from an intestinal *malrotation*? Could her bowel have a congenital defect in attachment, which allowed it to coil around on its own blood supply like the twisties that close a plastic bag? The twisting cuts off the blood supply to the area of the bowel that it supports. *Yes, she could have a malrotation,* I thought, *but that condition is exceedingly rare, and the X ray should be diagnostic for suspicion for that entity.*

Could Jamala have developed an intolerance to premature formula? Her abdominal tenderness contradicted that diagnosis. Perhaps she had a generalized infection that made her gut motility slow down, a condition that we call an *ileus*? Bloody stools, however, don't usually accompany a simple ileus.

Unfortunately the situation suggested to me necrotizing enterocolitis as the first three diagnoses at the top of the differential diagnostic list. I ordered a STAT abdominal X ray to evaluate what was going on inside the infant's belly. The X ray was absolutely diagnostic for necrotizing enterocolitis, complete with *pneumatosis intestinalis* and portal air.[1] No doubt about the diagnosis. The real question was how bad was it? Necrotizing enterocolitis, or NEC in JCAHO-approved medical shorthand, is the bane of neonatal units. It is an infectious and/or inflammatory condition of the bowel wall with an acute, sometimes fulminating, onset. Although term infants can develop NEC, it is ordinarily a disease of extremely preterm infants. Throughout the last four decades multiple risk factors for NEC, including low blood sugar, rotovirus infection, and maternal cocaine use, have been identified through retrospective studies.[2] Breast milk feeding seems to have some protective effect against NEC, but isn't a hundred percent effective, such as a vaccine might be. Most puzzling of all, some affected babies have no known risk factors. Perhaps there is a genetic component to susceptibility. NEC usually occurs sporadically, but occasionally neonatal units experience mini-epidemics of several babies at once. Most strangely, in some NICUs, NEC is almost unknown; in others, up to fifteen percent of extremely preterm infants are affected.

Often X-ray findings of pneumatosis intestinalis are equivocal or occur in infants who are minimally ill, whose clinical appearance is a mismatch with their X-ray findings, leaving doctors with many questions. Is it really pneumatosis, or is it merely air mixed with feces producing the soap bubble look? Should we stop feedings just to play it safe, or push on? Should we repeat the X ray in six hours, in twelve hours, or wait until tomorrow morning? Should we check the white count for signs of infection? Should we start antibiotics? Should we ask the pediatric surgeon to add his opinion?

Jamala's case wasn't a subtle one of NEC. The findings on Jamala's initial film were so blatant that a first-year pediatric or radiology resident could have made the diagnosis of necrotizing enterocolitis. It's what the radiologists call an "Aunt Minnie." If you see a lady coming out of Aunt Minnie's house, and she looks like Aunt Minnie, wears a hat and coat like Aunt Minnie's, and has a gait like Aunt Minnie, it's a good bet that the woman in question is Aunt Minnie.

Cocaine exposure undoubtedly played an important role in the cause of Jamala's disease. In vitro studies show that muscle cells, including muscle cells that line cardiac vessels, contract when exposed to cocaine. Jamala had been on the receiving end of cocaine two ways in utero. Maternal levels of lipid-soluble cocaine had passively crossed the placenta into Jamala's blood stream. Jamala had excreted the maternally acquired cocaine through her own urine into the amniotic fluid, and she then had swallowed the cocaine-laced amniotic fluid. The NEC-cocaine theory is that the muscles of the arteries leading to Jamala's bowel were repeatedly subjected to the constrictive powers of cocaine before she was born. When these muscle cells contracted, they constricted blood vessels and limited the flow of oxygen and nutrient-bearing blood to the bowel. We believe that this sequence may compromise the otherwise healthy bowel wall, setting up an inherent weakness. The theory is that once the newborn gut is required to break down food and absorb basic elements of nutrition, and is then exposed to bacterial colonization of the extrauterine environment, the stress causes inflammation, and infection follows, resulting in NEC.

Because complications of NEC frequently develop, neonatologists follow the progression of NEC very closely. We look for subtle changes in a newborn's clinical condition, vital signs, laboratory, and X-ray findings. Toxins released by dead and dying bowel and subsequent overwhelming bacterial infection may cause the infant's peripheral circulation to dilate, resulting in low blood pressure and rapid heart rate. Such toxins cause capillaries to leak. Fluid seeps out of the general circulation into the tissues causing severe edema. The baby becomes bloated. Dead bowel also releases *lactic acid* into the circulation and *metabolic acidosis* develops.

Jamala had no active bleeding, but her platelet count was very low. She required at least daily platelet transfusions to prevent the risk of hemorrhage. Jamala's clinical condition worsened, and respiratory failure ensued. On the second day of her illness, I was called to the bedside to insert a tube into her windpipe so that we could hook her up to a mechanical respirator in order to keep her alive. NEC also profoundly affects white blood count. A high white count is a sign of the body actively fighting off an infection. Conversely, a low white count *(neutropenia)* is a bad sign. A low white count in the presence of infection indicates that the bone marrow is stressed to the maximum and can't keep up with the demand for bacteria-fighting white cells. The mortality rate for infants with a low white count and active infection is very high. Jamala's white count was very low. By her third day of illness, her chance of survival was fair at best.

First Surgery

Treatment for NEC is initially medical. We give broad-spectrum antibiotics, support respiratory function, and stabilize blood pressure. Since the affected infant's nutrition can't be supported with oral feedings, *total parenteral nutrition (TPN),*[3] also called *hyperalimentation,* is administered. Initially TPN provides *intravenous* protein-sparing amino acids to prevent breakdown of the body's own tissues. TPN ultimately supports decent weight gain and growth even if a baby isn't receiving formula or breast milk.

We teach pediatric and surgical residents about five specific indications for surgical intervention in babies with NEC. All of these signs may show the presence of dead bowel or intestinal perforation. The most obvious indication for surgical intervention is the presence of free air in the belly, air not within the confines of the bowel. The presence of air on X ray below the diaphragm but not inside the bowel means that the bowel has developed a spontaneous hole. From the hole, fecal material spills out into the normally sterile abdominal cavity. The other indications for surgery are persistence of low *platelets*, development of severe metabolic acidosis, and redness of the abdominal wall. A bowel loop that doesn't move or change in size or shape from one X-ray film to the others over the course of several days is the fifth sign. Life and living organisms constantly change. The loop of bowel doesn't change because it is dead.

We ordered serial films to track the progression of Jamala's disease, ever hopeful that the next film would herald the beginnings of recovery. Yet we feared seeing progression of the disease instead. About the ninth film taken, three days into her illness, I saw the ominous football sign,[4] an oval lucency in the center of the film, indicating an intestinal perforation had occurred. The infection had attacked the bowel wall, eaten away at it, and thinned it, making a hole clearly evident. Air, contaminated bowel contents, blood, and intestinal juices were leaking into her belly. We knew that without surgery Jamala surely wouldn't survive, and even with prompt surgery she might still die. As soon as I recognized the perforation, I called Dr. Bellman. To his credit he came in immediately and met with Jamala's parents. Bellman told them of the urgent need for surgery, and described what he would do when he opened up Jamala's belly in the operating room.

"I'll look at the entire bowel. Once I locate the hole, I'll remove the segment with the hole and any other portions of her gut that look dead. Since her bowel is probably too friable (I doubted the parents knew what that meant) to try to hook up the two loose ends after I take out the diseased portion, it will be necessary to make a diverting *ostomy* (another word the family had probably never heard before). Then I'll bring the end of the bowel to the outside surface of the abdomen so that Jamala can have bowel movements. Jamala will return to the NICU with an ostomy. Unfortunately she'll have to wear a bag for a while."

Tasha B's eyes opened wide. *Bag.* Now she recognized what Dr. Bellman was talking about. Her cousin Derek had an ostomy when he got shot in a drive-by. He wore a bag for three months before he could get rid of it. I could tell she didn't like what she was hearing. An ostomy is a frightening prospect for anyone of any age.

"The bag will remain in place for at least six weeks," Dr. Bellman continued. "Until her bowel is hooked back together again, her nutrition may not be optimal. I feel pretty sure she'll continue to need intravenous nutrition in addition to formula. She's got a very long road ahead of her, with the constant risk of infection and liver damage from the TPN." He paused and sighed. "I have to be truthful. Your baby's outlook isn't good."

Tasha and her boyfriend nodded in agreement with the doctor, but it was obvious they didn't understand even half of the surgeon's words, much less the severity of the situation. Too bad Peggy Lou hadn't been employed as our nurse practitioner at that time. Had she been in on the conference with Jamala's parents, the conversation might have taken a different turn. When Dr. Bellman concluded by announcing that Jamala's outlook isn't good, Peggy Lou would have interjected in a very Southern tone, "Dr. Bellman, are you saayin' that Jamala mahght die?" Frequently the physician talks over the patient's head, using medical terms that might as well be a foreign language. The doctor may also present a one-sided conversation and not engage with the family, and therefore miss the fact that they don't understand.

Peggy Lou was an expert at body language and facial expression. She instinctively knew when the doctor was using medical terminology or was skirting a serious issue. Her perceptive sense was a gift. If there was an eight hundred pound silent gorilla in the room, Peggy Lou would take it down. She interrupted the flow of conversation to ask clarifying questions on behalf of the family, questions she knew they had but were embarrassed to ask, or questions they should have had in response to what the doctor had said. Rather than being a distraction, her interjections and well-placed questions rendered the conference more valuable to both the family and the doctor. But Peggy Lou wouldn't start working with us for another ten years, and I didn't and still don't speak body language. So when Dr. Bellman left, I asked Tasha and Antoine to repeat what Dr. Bellman told them, and if they believed she would be okay.

"Yes, as long as she has the surgery."

"She'll be fine in a few weeks." They agreed with each other.

It probably didn't matter that their understanding was limited since there was no other choice for Jamala other than the operation. Without the surgery she would definitely die. Surgery might give her a chance to live. The details of how sick she would be before she recovered or how sick she'd be before she died were unknown and therefore irrelevant. There was simply no alternative course to pursue. Jamala remained in surgery for four hours, which wasn't a good sign. Bellman was fast. He was known as the "surgeon's surgeon." A simple bowel surgery with an isolated perforation doesn't take that long to repair unless the baby has problems with blood pressure, breathing, or excessive bleeding. If that had been the case, Bellman would have put in a panicked call to me to come help manage Jamala's blood pressure and oxygenation status. He hadn't called. When Jamala was finally brought back to the NICU, Bellman updated me, and then gave the waiting family the bad news about the condition of the bowel, the ostomy, and the stormy course ahead.

But he didn't remove all hope for recovery. No doctor ever wants to remove all hope. But was Bellman really hopeful, or was he hiding what he suspected from me, from the infant's parents, perhaps even from himself? We medical professionals excel at self-delusion. We know the live-or-die statistics that cover the range of the diseases we deal with every day. But if the mortality rate for X disease is ninety percent, we may choose to emphasize to the family the ten percent who survive. Is that false hope? I myself have told parents that somebody has to make up the ten percent, why not their baby? Did I have the right to assume that Jamala would be among the non-surviving ninety percent? Of course not, but I certainly had the responsibility to tell her mother about the unfortunate ninety percent. And parents look at statistics differently than physicians. Mothers and fathers are not mathematicians. And their babies are definitely not statistics. A baby doesn't survive in percentages. For the individual baby, survival is either one hundred percent or zero. The father of a fragile twenty-two-week premature baby that statistically had a slim-to-none chance of survival, but whose family insisted on intensive care, once expressed this thought to me quite poignantly. I had told him that his baby Kenyatta had less than a one percent chance of survival.

He said, "Dr. Sacks, the problem is that you and me look at this situation from different aspects." "Me and my wife see our little baby as he is now, alive and breathing. So we figure he has a chance to survive, and we want everything possible done to help him. When we look at him, we don't see a tiny miniature baby in an incubator. We see our son cured and running around the house chasing the dog, just like we thought he would before he was born too soon. You and the other doctors and nurses see only your statistics saying he won't survive. Don't look at my son as a statistic. Please don't do that, Doctor. Kenyatta isn't a statistic. He's our son. Try to look at him like we do, as our unique baby with his own special needs and a chance to survive." Kenyatta's father unknowingly but wisely set me straight on that point. And although Kenyatta died two weeks later from multiple system failure, and although parental hope springs eternal, medical statistics don't lie. As doctors we must have total respect for that father's point of view even as we balance it with the realities of current science.

Perhaps Bellman regretted not simply closing up Jamala's abdomen and admitting there wasn't anything more he could do. I suspected that given the fact that Jamala was a more mature and larger infant with no intrinsic lung disease or neurological problems, that Bellman erred on the side of trying to save her. The problem was that that little glimmer of hope blinded him, as well as Jamala's parents.

Over the next week my partners and I continued to provide full medical support: mechanical ventilation, broad-spectrum antibiotics, blood and platelet transfusions, and TPN. Jamala's condition stabilized somewhat, but her white count rose to very high levels raising suspicion of ongoing infection despite broad-spectrum antibiotics. Her platelet count remained quite low despite daily platelet transfusions. Meanwhile Dr. Bellman went on a previously planned vacation. Ten days after Jamala's initial surgery, she wasn't getting any better. As a non-surgeon neonatologist I hadn't anything to offer but more of the same therapy, which seemed ineffective. I prevailed upon Dr. Bellman's partner, Dr. Jack Dafney, who wasn't a formally trained pediatric surgeon, to go for that planned second look. Since this was a semi-elective procedure, we couldn't take Jamala to the operating room without parental permission. Obtaining that permission was very problematic. Her parents hadn't called or visited since Jamala's first surgery. Social workers' and nurses' multiple phone calls to the contact numbers the couple had left with us didn't reach them. Marianna took the next step. She asked the police to locate them. Without Tasha's permission for surgery, we would have had to obtain a court order to proceed.

After a delay of a few hours, Tasha at last called in. I obtained a telephone consent for the second surgery. For such consent the parent has to repeat to a second person their verbal permission for surgery. This was (and is) not truly informed consent, but it was the best we could do in a bad situation. Tasha and Antoine had no questions. My holier-than-thou moral antennae up as usual, I suspected they were high on cocaine. I am a great fan of Maimonides, the twelfth-century Spanish rabbinic scholar and doctor, who served as the court physician to the grand vizier of Egypt. Maimonides composed a *Prayer for the Physician*.[5] The Albert Einstein School of Medicine and several other medical schools use it in place of the more ancient and better known Hippocratic Oath,[6] which many physicians believe is totally outdated. One key phrase of Maimonides' prayer rang in my ears as I dealt with Jamala's parents: *Almighty God, preserve the strength of my body and my soul that they ever be ready to cheerfully help and support rich and poor, good and bad, enemy as well as friend. In the sufferer let me see only the human being.* I reminded myself of Maimonides' words as I finished my telephone conversation with Jamala's cocaine addicted mother.

Second Surgery

The second surgery took far less time than the first. *Maybe that's a sign that the findings are good,* I lied to myself. Maybe Dr. Bellman was right, and the questionable areas of the bowel had recovered. When Jamala was brought back from the second surgery, her abdomen was no longer distended; it was flat, like a model's. Dr. Dafney accompanied the baby and once again the news wasn't good.

"Most of the bowel, from her stomach to her rectum was dead," he explained. "It fell apart in my hands. That's why she was still acting like she was infected. I'm sorry, Linda, there wasn't anything I could do." Dr. Dafney paused, swallowed hard, and awkwardly continued. "So I removed all of her bowel. All that's left is her stomach, and that's where I created the new ostomy."

"What! Are you for real? Why did you do that? For heaven's sake, why didn't you just close her up, bring her back, and let her die?" In my frustration I forgot the sage advice of my dear friend and business mentor George Monroe: "Sweetheart, when somebody screws up badly," my MBA-holding friend used to remind me, "and does something really stupid, just ask him: Tell me what you were thinking when you . . . instead of announcing that he is a complete moron for what he did."

I couldn't believe what Jack had told me, that he'd removed all of Jamala's intestines except for her stomach. And that he expected me and my neonatal colleagues to resume her care from that point on! I was furious, and I made no attempt to hide my anger and frustration. George wouldn't have been proud of me.

"What are we supposed to do now? She can't survive long term like this." I didn't add, although I thought to myself, *You idiot, what the hell were you thinking?* I shook my head as I spoke. I probably also rolled my eyes, an unfortunate gesture I make involuntarily when I'm aggravated. Psychologists say eye-rolling indicates contempt. "She's not a candidate for an eventual experimental bowel transplant, is she?"

"No, that won't work either," he replied. "The blood vessels supplying her intestine were all clotted, so I had to remove them as well. There is no blood supply to hook up to a transplanted bowel."

I also knew that Jamala's chaotic social situation eliminated any consideration of this kind of as yet unproven procedure.[7] "So what do I tell her parents?" I asked him.

Experience had taught me that this particular surgeon didn't stick around for a difficult conversation with parents. But to give the surgeon some benefit in a sad situation, it was questionable if Tasha and Antoine would even show up at the hospital that evening.

"I'd just tell them there wasn't anything more we could have done, and nothing more going forward. Then I'd remove her from the ventilator, stop her antibiotics, keep her comfortable, and let nature take its course. I'd let her die." With those curt words Dr. Dafney made a hasty exit.

Two hours later, surprisingly, Jamala's parents arrived at the hospital. Sadly, however, they were under the influence of some mood-altering drug. They smelled like cheap liquor and reeked of stale cigarettes. Given the fact that I blamed them for Jamala's condition, I tried to explain the hopelessness of the situation with as much compassion as I could muster. Maimonides' words pounding in my head, I went over the details of the second surgery. I hope I said I was sorry somewhere in the conversation.

"The entire bowel—all of Jamala's intestines—was dead," I said. "The surgeon removed all of it. A person can't live without intestines to absorb nutrition from food. I'm sorry, but Jamala is going to die no matter what else we do." I waited a few moments for the information to sink in. Jamal's mother and father remained silent. "I think the best thing for Jamala is to stop all aggressive therapy, including the ventilator. We can keep her comfortable with morphine until she dies. Continuing with antibiotics and the respirator will only prolong her suffering."

Then, all of a sudden: "No. You can't do that." Tasha was angry. What right did she have to be angry? Jamala's parents refused to discuss the situation any further. They emphatically forbade me to discontinue support. They told me that Jamala would get better. "She's strong, she's a fighter, she'll make it," Tasha said unrealistically but with conviction.

I hear comments similar to these all the time. And yes, some babies are stronger than others. Some babies fight harder to stay alive. I'm not always correct when I say that a baby will probably die. My crystal ball doesn't always see clearly. But this case was a physical impossibility for long-term survival. It was obvious that Jamala's parents didn't understand what I had told them. I considered—briefly—the possibility that they had religious faith greater than mine. But I doubted that—they didn't mention that God would heal Jamala, a sentiment I had heard countless times before in hopeless situations. A sentiment I had learned to respect even if I disagreed with it. A sentiment that once dismissed by the doctor, fractures the relationship with the baby's family.

Legally Jamala's mother still had decision-making authority for her baby. If we went to court over the issue of her inability to parent on account of substance abuse, DFCS would probably ask for removal of custody. The court might even appoint a guardian ad litum whose job it would be to represent the best interests of the child in any conflict between the physicians and DFCS. My experience when the agency has custody of a child had been that withdrawal of support was never requested, no matter how clear the futility of further treatment was or how severe the continued suffering. Thereby DFCS forces a court hearing in which the hospital must bring suit to discontinue support on moral grounds: continued treatment isn't only futile, it is cruel and inhumane. At that time an infant ethics committee did not exist at our hospital. Although the first official children's bioethics committees originated in 1984, Pine Grove Hospital wouldn't have its own general bioethics committee until 1988.[8] Although bioethics committees can be helpful in resolving ethical dilemmas in medicine, they do come under criticism. As one doctor put it, the responsibility for decisions is diffused: "It's a lot more reassuring to play one-fifth God—to share the decision with (four) other people."[9] The type of problem we faced with Jamala, however, was one of the less frequent ones anticipated by the founders of infant bioethics committees. The original role of the bioethics committee was to aid in decision making when it was the parent who wanted to discontinue or not to initiate lifesaving support because of risk of future handicap and/or futility, and it was the doctors who felt initiation or continuation of therapy was warranted. The committees were an outgrowth of the clinical situations that produced the now-defunct Baby Doe Law, an amendment to the Child Abuse Prevention and Treatment Act of 1978. The law addressed the few specific instances in which care could legally be withheld.

The more common reason today for bioethics consultation in neonatology is the absolute reverse—the desire of physicians to withdraw futile therapy in the face of the family's insistence on its continuation. Parents may be unable to accept the inevitable. They may distrust the baby's physicians. Firm religious beliefs or their own selfish interests may stand in the way of a decision to end futile care for their child. It is preferable to avoid a power struggle between the family and the staff. Bioethics committees help the two sides hear and acknowledge each other's viewpoints, and to resolve the issue through continued dialogue. Although pediatricians are under no obligation to render useless care just because parents request it, most physicians caring for newborns at the time of Jamala's case were afraid of the Baby Doe Law.[10] Jamala's condition clearly fell under provision C: "the provision of such treatment would be virtually futile in terms of the survival of the infant and the treatment itself under such circumstances would be inhumane." And yet, as physicians, we were afraid to act. Big Brother would be watching. And he'd posted hotlines to the federal government in every hospital caring for newborns. He'd employed "God squads" to descend into our nurseries to investigate. He'd threatened prosecution and loss of federal funds for violation of his mandates.

The three attending neonatologists, Cynthia James, Naomi Trent, and I, met the following morning to discuss what to do. We were not brave enough to stop Jamala's antibiotics, knowing that she would die of infection if we did. No one of the three of us was willing to withdraw any aspects of medical treatment against parental wishes. Trapped, we continued all therapeutic modalities. Jamala, also trapped, was heavily sedated with morphine so she wouldn't feel any pain. At least when we looked at her we perceived that she wasn't feeling any pain.

Jamala's parents disappeared again. They didn't even call to see how she was progressing. They seemed to know just how long they could stay away without being subjected to charges of abandonment, and wouldn't jeopardize losing the baby by staying away too long. They seemed to know how to play the system well. This infuriated us, but just as Jamala was helpless, so were we.

After another fourteen days of antibiotics, Jamala's infection was apparently cured. Taking out her dead bowel removed the source of infection. She'd been weaned off the ventilator and didn't even require supplemental oxygen. To look at her she appeared healthy. TPN had kept her alive; she was even starting to put on real weight. She was very cute, very responsive. She was a favorite of the nurses. They doted on her and brought her pretty outfits to wear. What were we supposed to do? What was going to happen to Jamala? What kind of future did she face? She had no bowel to absorb food. She wasn't a candidate, not then, not ever, for a bowel transplant because of the extent of her previous surgery and her family situation. Eventually, in weeks or months or two years at the outside, the toxic side effects of long-term TPN administration, the same TPN that currently kept her alive, would destroy her liver and she would die. More likely she would succumb to an intercurrent infection before that time. Should we keep her in the hospital on TPN until that time, on the slim-to-none chance that a new bowel transplant technique might be developed during the interim? While infants occasionally are discharged home on TPN, Jamala couldn't in good medical conscience be treated at home under the less than watchful eyes and less than caring hands of crack-head parents. Moreover, in our city of 250,000 no medically suitable foster homes capable of caring for a baby like Jamala were available.

Our moral cowardice and failure to make tough decisions up to that point had created an ethical monster. That monster menaced Jamala. Her suffering sat uneasily on our shoulders. Her fate was our responsibility. We placed our poor decision on the back burner, trying not to think about it. Instead we measured Jamala's blood chemistries to make sure they remained within normal limits. Although she was going to die, we didn't want her to die of an electrolyte imbalance, something we could easily control. Jamala continued on TPN for another month, growing well, and not developing any blood stream infections. Her parents visited once every nine or ten days, stayed a short time, sneaking out when they thought no one was looking. What few questions they asked were irrelevant. Their conversations with our nurses consisted of silly comments and their perceived complaints about the care their daughter was receiving. They demonstrated no understanding of Jamala's health problems and poor prognosis. The nursing staff could barely tolerate their visits. Once the parents left, the nurses gossiped about them for days. Rightly or wrongly, out of our frustration and anger we gave up any further true attempts to communicate with Jamala's parents.

In the absence of a bioethics committee, we met with the hospital chaplain for guidance regarding Jamala's fate. The decision we made was painful, but the true question was pain now or pain later. We would stop TPN. We would keep Jamala comfortable with intravenous fluid and pain medications as needed. She still had a central catheter—a secure, surgically placed intravenous line for her intravenous fluids, which would now consist basically of sugar water and salt. Since she had no gut beyond the stomach we couldn't even offer her comfort feedings. Nurse Robin discovered that Jamala liked Dum-Dums, small sugary lollipops. She mouthed them as the nurses held them for her. The cherry flavored ones were her favorite. The melted lollipop juice came out in Jamala's ostomy bag.

Jamala's parents continued to stay away. They hadn't come in nearly two weeks. We didn't try to contact them. Why bother? I tried not to think about Maimonides' advice.

Thirteen days after the decision to stop TPN, Jamala's central catheter clotted off. It had been inserted during her second surgery, and it was her fourth one. To place another central catheter would require a procedure in the OR. Since intravenous fluids were only prolonging her dying, not saving her life, we decided not to restart the line. The nurses tried to put in a peripheral intravenous line, which was hardly a heroic measure. Jamala's arms and legs were swollen from poor nutrition, and her tiny veins were hard to find. The IVs didn't last more than a day or two. Consequently a day came when multiple attempts to stick her to start another IV line failed. With no intravenous line, no intestines, no way to provide even maintenance fluid, what should we do now? We regrouped to discuss the dismal situation. The choices left to Jamala— and to us—were pitiful. If we stopped her fluids, she'd dehydrate and die within days. To continue fluids, even without adequate nutrition, would require anesthesia and surgery for line placement. And without the protein of TPN, she would become more bloated from malnutrition.

She could live that way for another few weeks. But in the end, she would still die.

The moment of ultimate truth had arrived. We had to choose between prolonging ineffective therapy and possible suffering, or stopping therapy. We decided to stop all fluids and to continue lollipops for pleasure. For the next four days NICU nurses took turns holding Jamala and rocking her. They provided round-the-clock cuddling, contact, and comfort. She was never alone, whether in or out of her bed, and she was rarely without her cherry Dum-Dum lollipop to give her additional comfort, unless she was asleep. Jamala's overall condition weakened. We debated whether to call her parents. Much as we disliked them, they were still her parents. As such they deserved an opportunity to say good-bye. Maimonides would agree.

So we called them on a Monday morning. On Wednesday afternoon they showed up. By this time Jamala was close to death. I explained to them that the end of the road was near. Much to my surprise they appeared to understand what was happening. They placed a special prayer cloth on their daughter's bassinet. Tearful, they left for a short break with a solemn promise to return soon.

Two hours later they returned as promised. Their demeanor was totally different. They were high, presumably on cocaine. The Doctors Jekyll had turned into the Hydes. Arrogantly they demanded to know why their baby couldn't be fed more than just a lollipop. As the physician in charge, I attempted to explain everything again, starting from the beginning. But it was of no use. Jamala's parents became hostile and stormed out of the unit in an angry huff.

Jamala died later that night, surrounded by the doctors and nurses of the NICU, the only people who truly cared about her.

Exactly twelve months later Tasha B resurfaced in our NICU as the mother of yet another even more premature baby. Antoine was out of the picture. Tasha had had only one prenatal visit, and she was HIV positive, as was her premature newborn. It was the early days of HIV therapy; only one drug was available to combat the AIDS virus, AZT or zidovadine. More effective medications were in the research phase. Triple drug therapy was unheard of. Administration of large doses of antiviral medication at the time of delivery for the prevention of HIV transmission to the newborn, and continued treatment of the baby, had yet to be discovered.[11] Testing HIV positive was a death sentence for Tasha and in all likelihood for Jamala's little sister as well.

1. Pneumatosis intestinalis appears on an X ray as multiple soap-bubble–like areas within the wall of the intestines. The bubbles represent air trapped between the mucosal lining of the gut and the muscular layer that encircles it. Portal air appears as Christmas tree–like bare branches sprouting in the normally solid gray liver shadow. This arboreal phenomenon represents air outlining the portal veins that course through the liver. Air isn't a normal resident in either the bowel wall or portal venous system. Air should be found only in the lumen of the bowel. Either pneumatosis intestinalis or portal air in a newborn equals necrotizing enterocolitis.

2. These factors also include a history of birth asphyxia, prematurity, *cyanotic* congenital heart disease, low blood pressure, *polycythemia*, *patent ductus arteriosus*, exposure to indomethacin, and recent blood transfusion.

3. This clear yellow solution contains sugar, minerals, vitamins, elemental hydrolyzed protein. Fats are delivered in a milky-white companion solution called Intralipid. Developed in the late 1960's by a pediatric surgeon in Philadelphia, TPN has saved the lives of hundreds of thousands of children, especially tiny premature infants and babies who require complex abdominal or cardiac surgery. TPN is expensive; each bag is good for only twenty-four hours, is customized for the needs of its recipient, and must be assembled sterilely in the pharmacy under a laminar flow hood.

4. With a practiced eye one can discern a grayish oval-shaped lucency in the middle of the belly film. The imaginary lacing of the football runs from the left lower quadrant of the abdomen to the right upper quadrant diagonally across the film. It is the outline of the falciform ligament—the remnant of the umbilical vein that once extended from the placenta into the inferior vena cava, the former supply route for oxygen and nutrition to

the infant as she grew in the womb. Normally not visible on an X ray, the ligament becomes visible when its tissue density is highlighted by free air on either side of it.

5. Some authorities believe the prayer was really written in the eighteenth century by Marcus Herz, a German physician who only attributed the prayer to the renowned physician. When I first read about Dr. Herz's reputed authorship, I was terribly disappointed. For me, it will always be Maimonides' composition.

6. I swear by Apollo the Physician and Asclepius and Hygieia and Panaceia and all the gods, and goddesses, making them my witnesses, that I will fulfill according to my ability and judgment this oath and this covenant: To hold him who has taught me this art as equal to my parents and to live my life in partnership with him, and if he is in need of money to give him a share of mine, and to regard his offspring as equal to my brothers in male lineage and to teach them this art—if they desire to learn it— without fee and covenant; to give a share of precepts and oral instruction and all the other learning to my sons and to the sons of him who has instructed me and to pupils who have signed the covenant and have taken the oath according to medical law, but to no one else.

I will apply dietic measures for the benefit of the sick according to my ability and judgment; I will keep them from harm and injustice. I will neither give a deadly drug to anybody if asked for it, nor will I make a suggestion to this effect. Similarly I will not give to a woman an abortive remedy. In purity and holiness I will guard my life and my art. I will not use the knife, not even on sufferers from stone, but will withdraw in favor of such men as are engaged in this work. Whatever houses I may visit, I will come for the benefit of the sick, remaining free of all intentional injustice, of all mischief and in particular of sexual relations with both female and male persons, be they free or slaves.

What I may see or hear in the course of treatment or even outside of the treatment in regard to the life of men, which on no account one must spread abroad, I will keep myself holding such things shameful to be spoken about. If I fulfill this oath and don't violate it, may it be granted to me to enjoy life and art, being honoured with fame among all men for all time to come; if I transgress it and swear falsely, may the opposite of all this be my lot.

7. Today small bowel transplants remain high risk, but no longer experimental. However, patients are carefully chosen, and social situation is

considered. Such a high-risk procedure requires constant attention and follow-up.

8. American Academy of Pediatrics and Infant Bioethics Task Force and Consultants, "Guidelines for Infant Bioethics Committees," *Pediatrics* 74 (1984): 306–310.

9. R. Fox and J. Swazey, *The Courage to Fail* (Chicago: University of Chicago Press, 1978).

10. A. Brett, L. McCullough, "Where Patients Request Specific Interventions," *New England Journal of Medicine* 315 (1986): 1347–51.

11. Current management of HIV pregnant women with triple drug therapy, large doses of zidovadine intrapartum, selective use of cesarian section, and treatment of the baby for six weeks with zidovadine has reduced the mother-to-baby transmission rate from twenty-five percent to close to zero.

6

UNEXPECTED DISASTER

Meconium

"Dr. Sacks, please get over to Remington Hospital right now. The baby for transport has gone bad. Real bad. The transport team needs you STAT."

My 1980's beeper screamed voice messages only. Text messages and silent screen call-back numbers didn't exist yet. Since most pages were from nursing personnel who were aware that the page recipient might be in a public arena, the usual transmittal was a softly spoken request to call the neonatal unit. Politely, almost apologetically, a nurse's voice might say "Please call extension 7615 when you get a chance; I have some lab results for you." The current message, however, was unlike others I had received throughout the evening. Its urgency scared me. The speaker, Jeanine Walburg, normally a very coolheaded and experienced professional, sounded uncharacteristically desperate. To make matters worse, I received the troublesome message at a most inconvenient time. I was shopping in a local twenty-four-hour pharmacy located directly across the street from Pine Grove Hospital. My mission at the drugstore was child-centered, namely picking up a promised candy bar with my son, Noah. The two of us had just left Pine Grove's neonatal unit after I admitted an infant with a minor issue. We were in the process of choosing wisely from the many unhealthy snacks on display next to the cash register near the store exit. Junk food was definitely not a concern in the 1980's. The obesity epidemic lay dormant, awaiting discovery. Aspartame and Splenda were chemicals in the lab, not part of our daily lives. Public schools still allowed recess, dodge ball, jungle gyms, and choosing up individuals for teams. The good-old days of childhood were filled with fun, competition, excitement, and a small but definite risk of bodily and psychological harm.

In the early 1980's after hours we neonatologists took call from our homes. When summoned back in the early evening, I sometimes took my youngest son, four-year-old Noah, back with me because he loved to go. I wasn't sure this counted as quality time, but Noah enjoyed the trip, as well as the attention he got from the nurses. On these medical sojourns with me he enjoyed sitting at the nurses' station, playing with his beloved Lego blocks, which he toted around in a plastic zip-lock bag. He made friends easily; the nurses thought he was darling.

"Do you have any spare pennies or nickels for me?" Noah would ask, turning his huge wide-set, long-lashed hazel eyes to the charge nurse, his latest feminine conquest. I was mortified, but the staff found him amusing. They usually obliged, and consequently he frequently returned home with a dollar or two in pennies, nickels, and dimes: a successful trip by Noah's standards. With all this exposure to exciting medicine, I had high hopes that he might eventually choose a career in medicine. However, in college he lasted only six months as a premed student: "Too many labs, not enough fun, Mom." Up until the frantic page, the pace of the evening had been leisurely, and so we had gone across the street for the candy break before returning home. However, after that worrisome page from Jeanine the tempo abruptly changed. I was definitely in a hurry. Fortunately there was no line for the cashier. I paid for the chocolate bar and within sixty seconds of the page I found myself driving the two and a half miles home as rapidly as I dared with such precious cargo on board and so little time to spare for the trip to the other hospital.

I pulled into my driveway. Opening the garage door with the remote control, I told Noah, "Go inside, sweetie, and tell Daddy I am going back to the hospital for an emergency." When I saw Noah disappear safely into the house, I shut the garage door with the remote control. Pedal to the metal, I rushed on to Remington Hospital, which was only a mile and a half away from my home. With no traffic, I exceeded the posted speed limit. Luckily I made both green lights. While I was willing to speed, I wasn't willing to run a red light on a major highway. A dead or maimed neonatologist is of no use to a sick baby.

Some background to explain the urgent page. Earlier in the evening, while at Pine Grove, I had received a call initiating the transport of a sick baby from Remington to Pine Grove's neonatal unit. In those days our group of neonatologists didn't have admitting privileges at Remington, only consultants' privileges. Our pediatric colleagues at Remington could consult us as necessary. We would then go over to evaluate the infant about whom they had concerns. If the baby was sick enough to need more than a second visit from us, we transferred the child to our unit at Pine Grove. We didn't have privileges to admit patients or to attend deliveries at Remington, even though Remington did forty-eight percent of the deliveries in town, more than either of the other two maternity centers. An ugly story lay behind the denial of admitting privileges.

There had been intense professional rivalry between the two neigh-boring hospitals involving just about every medical issue imaginable: academics versus faith-based medical care, medical specialists versus fam-ily-oriented physicians, high tech versus high touch. When one hospital created a new service line, the other one followed suit, even if the service was in name only. Each new expensive piece of modern medical technol-ogy was duplicated as soon as possible. The administration of Pine Grove, the hospital that partially paid my salary, refused to permit its neonatolo-gists to have full privileges (which would have included admission privi-leges) at other hospitals. It seemed to me that pride and potential hospital revenues outstripped the importance of patient welfare, which meant that bragging rights to having the only *level III* neonatal intensive care unit superseded the value of babies' lives. Competition over funding trumped the cooperation and collaboration necessary to curtail rapidly escalating costs of health care. As the budget for advertising at each hospital grew bigger each year, the relationship between the two administrations grew more adversarial. The local press had a field day with these stories of competition. But because newspapers more often raise questions than answer them, the general public didn't understand why the two hospitals appeared to be at each others' throats.

The subject of the urgent page calling me to Remington was Cameron C. Her mother had delivered her vaginally through amniotic fluid containing thick *meconium*, probably because she was two weeks overdue. Meconium is the scientific name for fetal stool. It is composed of sloughed intestinal epithelial cells, lanugo (fine baby hair), mucus, desquamated fetal skin cells, swallowed amniotic fluid, and bile. Dark green from its bile content, sometimes nearly black in appearance, meconium has a very tenacious texture, best described as akin to moist yeast dough between the first and second risings, or cheap hair gel. The majority of infants who pass meconium before birth are at least thirty-eight weeks gestation (full term being forty weeks gestation). Beyond forty weeks the incidence of meconium passage in-utero rises exponentially.[1] Once passed by the fetus, the dreaded meconium mixes with the amniotic fluid present in the uterus.[2] The final appearance of the fluid ranges from slightly green tinged to pea soup. Why should a fetus pass stool before birth? Prior to 1990 the answer consistently offered by plaintiff's attorneys was fetal distress, in other words, a fetus in great trouble. In experimental animal models, depriving a term fetus of oxygen leads to passage of meconium before birth, as well as to gasping breaths in utero. The gasps suck meconium-contaminated amniotic fluid into the fetal lungs. There is no way to be certain that this animal theory holds true in humans as well, and certainly there is no ethical way to experiment.

The weight of scientific evidence today points to fetal distress as only one of several theories about the cause of antepartum meconium passage. Another theory holds that passage of meconium shows a fetus adequately coping with stress, rather than one succumbing to stress. The stressed but adequately coping fetus exhibits the diving reflex, a primitive reflex seen in mammals that spend long periods of time submerged in water, like seals and whales. This diving reflex redirects blood flow to essential organs: heart, brain, kidneys, and adrenal glands. Blood flow to non-essential organs such as muscle, skin, gut, and lungs (remember, in utero or underwater lungs are superfluous for respiration) is decreased. The human gut responds to this compromised flow with peristalsis, rhythmic contractions designed to expel intestinal contents. The contractions expel meconium, and the fetus defecates in utero. A third theory holds that the infant is simply getting ready for life outside the uterus. Passage of stool is a normal function, like the practicing of sucking, swallowing, and kicking before birth. Premature infants have delayed stooling patterns after birth, and rarely pass meconium before birth even if stressed. This latter fact would seem to give some credence to this practice-makes-perfect or *meconium happens* theory.

I didn't know why my patient Cameron had passed meconium before birth. She had required resuscitation immediately after birth because she hadn't made much of an effort to breathe. Her resuscitation had included the placing of a tube in her throat so that the doctor would be able to provide oxygen to her, and to breathe for her. I didn't know if he attempted to suction out the thick meconium from Cameron's throat before providing ventilation to her, as was the standard of care in the mid-1980's (and even today). The resuscitation had been handled by the anesthesiologist, Dr. Jerry Knight. By virtue of his specialty training, Dr. Knight was by far the most skilled person at resuscitation in the delivery room that evening.

The pediatrician, who in any case wasn't as skilled in resuscitation as Dr. Knight, hadn't been called to attend the delivery. I later discovered that he had no knowledge of the emergency. Mrs. C's membranes had ruptured just prior to delivery, so the meconium was an unpleasant surprise. Hence there had been no time to summon the pediatrician from home. In retrospect, Dr. Knight actually had made the call requesting transport to the Pine Grove neonatal intensive care unit after the resuscitation. Since I was physically present in the unit when Dr. Knight called, he had spoken directly to me. Had I not been right there, I wonder if he would've asked to speak to a neonatologist.

We routinely received many transport calls from local physicians in other communities. Many times they spoke only to the charge nurse, never asking to confer with the neonatologist. Sometimes the request for transfer was even nurse-to-nurse, keeping the doctors totally out of the communication loop. At times this occurred because the referring doctor was physically tied up working on the sick newborn. At other times I suspected the referring doctor might be afraid that his lack of sophisticated knowledge about sick newborns would show in a conversation with a neonatal nurse or neonatologist.

The call regarding Cameron had come in while I was still in the NICU with my son Noah, finishing up my paperwork, before heading out for the candy break. Therefore, I was available to take the call directly. Normally I'd have been at home. A male voice had told me the salient facts.

I had responded, "Is she stable? Do I need to come over right now, or can you wait for the transport team?" Cognizant of the fact that I had consulting, although not admission, privileges at Remington, I had offered to go over immediately to consult. The team might have to be called in from home, and that would take up to an additional thirty minutes for them to get to Pine Grove, pick up their equipment, and depart for the short ride to Remington. If the infant had been described as unstable, I would've called my husband to come pick up our son, then I would've gone directly to Remington.

The caller responded, "No, she's stable. I've got the situation under control. She's going to need a ventilator, however, and we don't manage ventilated babies over here. Just send the team. She'll be fine temporarily on our ventilator until then."

The physician had told me that he had already contacted the pediatrician, Dr. Al Boucher, who had agreed with the plan. The hour was getting late, and I knew that a ventilated infant, even if stable, would take longer to admit and stabilize once he got to Pine Grove. Noah was still with me, so I left the unit to make a quick stop for candy and then to drop him off at home. I intended to turn around immediately and come back. I'd return well before the team got back with the sick infant. Noah and I departed for the promised side trip for candy, but I was STAT-paged, and the trip abruptly ended as I took him home and turned around to go to Remington.

On my arrival at Remington I realized I didn't know if the infant was still in labor and delivery, or had been moved to the special care nursery. I had no cell phone, as they hadn't yet been invented. It was after hours and the administrative offices lining the hallway, in which I might have found a phone, were locked. There were no house phones located in the corridor. The labor and delivery suite was on the first floor, very close to the doctors' entrance to the hospital. I stopped there first, which was a logical choice, but incorrect; the baby wasn't there. I rushed up the stairs to the nursery on the third floor. Say what you will about the interruptions of today's communication devices such as cellular phones, but the fact is that they often save lives.

Emergency!

The sight that greeted me at the nursery's entrance will forever be hauntingly and indelibly etched in my memory. The Remington nursing staff of two, and the Pine Grove Hospital transport nurse and respiratory therapist were at the infant's bedside. One staff nurse was frantically attempting to start an *intravenous* line. The respiratory therapist was ventilating the infant with an *ambu* bag through a tube in the baby's throat, but the infant's chest was barely moving with each inflation. I could tell from the hand motions and the troubled expression on the therapist's face that she was using very high pressures. The baby's chest should have been expanding well, but clearly wasn't.

Although the infant was Caucasian, her color was a livid blotchy purple. Upward from the nipple line, her body was swollen, but the bloating wasn't fluid. It was subcutaneous air. Pressing on the skin of her upper chest yielded the same sensation as popping bubble wrap. Air had dissected out of her stiff lungs into her chest cavity causing life-threatening tension *pneumothoraces* (collapsed lungs). Under extreme pressure the air then made its way to the tissues beneath the skin of her chest, neck, and face. Meeting little resistance from the tissues, it dissected through. *Subcutaneous emphysema*, the medical name for this phenomenon, is not common in newborns. Although I had seen it a few times before,

I had never seen it to this extent. The baby's heart rate was about fifty, dangerously low for a newborn. Based on Cameron's clinical appearance, the transport nurse, Karen, had diagnosed her bilateral collapsed lungs. When Karen arrived, she also noted that although the staff nurses thought they were using one hundred percent oxygen to ventilate the baby, she was actually getting only room air of twenty-one percent oxygen. In the commotion of admitting a critically ill baby, the OR team hadn't turned on the wall outlet oxygen! The resuscitation bag was one of the self-inflating kinds. The advantage is that it will work without a compressed air or oxygen source so no time is lost hooking it up to a gas source. The disadvantage is that since it will work without an oxygen source, one has to remember to turn on the oxygen, or only room air flows through it. When we realized the error, Karen immediately turned on the oxygen and then placed needles in both sides of the baby's chest to begin to draw out the air. That was definitely a lifesaving move. It had been Karen who had called Jeanine to request that I come over ASAP. Karen, who later told me she had been terrified by the circumstances, felt instantly relieved when I arrived. But then it was my turn to be terrified.

Neonatologists generally have Type A personalities; it's the nature of the beast. We are take-command, do-it-yesterday types. In emergencies, however, we have to keep cool and take charge, or we would be completely ineffective. There is an ordered way to figure out what has gone wrong and to attempt its correction. The ABC's of resuscitation are airway, breathing, and circulation. In the critical situation with which we were faced, the first step was to ascertain that Cameron's breathing tube was still in the right place—in the trachea headed to the lungs—and not clogged with secretions. I could not be sure. Because there was no time for an X ray, and because an X ray would not show me if the tube was clogged or not, I pulled out the tube. It was clogged with sticky meconium, and was also a size smaller than appropriate for the infant's weight and degree of maturity. This missized tube rendered ventilation less effective, and increased the risk of clogging-off with meconium, Q.E.D.[3] Thorough direct suctioning of her trachea yielded a goodly amount of meconium. I replaced the tube with a clean one in a larger size and we resumed ventilation. The whole maneuver took little more than sixty seconds.

Based on the clinical scenario of subcutaneous emphysema, Karen had wisely guessed that Cameron had bilateral collapsed lungs. On account of partial plugging of small airways with meconium, her air sacs had ruptured.[4] The escaped air filled her chest, compressed her lungs, inhibited the return of blood into her heart, and prevented her heart from pumping effectively. Taking the path of least resistance, some of the air had also dissected into her skin. Through the needles Karen had inserted into each side of her chest, she sucked out massive quantities of air with a large syringe. It was a continuous flow, indicative of a large leak. I made preparations to give a round of drugs for Cameron's low heart rate, as well as to give fluid and bicarbonate before placing chest tubes. A labor and delivery nurse had been commandeered as an extra pair of hands. That nurse began cardiac compressions. The respiratory therapist continued ventilation. I placed an umbilical venous catheter as a secure intravenous access route. Then I gave *adrenalin* twice and pushed two doses of saline intravenously through the catheter. Only after giving the drugs and fluid did I insert bilateral chest tubes. Cameron responded to the team's actions with an increased heart rate and some semblance of blood flow to her body. She "pinked up" considerably, and made attempts at spontaneous breathing. I started an arterial line in her umbilicus for monitoring her blood gases, and the team sped off with Cameron for the seven-minute trip, code 3, lights and sirens, to Pine Grove Hospital.

For the next week, Cameron was critically ill. She had severe *meconium aspiration* syndrome and *pulmonary hypertension*. Her lung circulation had reacted to the periods without adequate oxygenation, as well as to the presence of meconium in her lungs, by maintaining after birth the high lung vascular pressures normally present in utero. The result was blood directed *away* from her lungs, preventing the blood from picking up oxygen for distribution to her body. During the first few days of Cameron's life, it was necessary to insert several more chest tubes to compensate for the multiple leaks in her brittle lungs. Her kidneys shut down for the first thirty-six hours. Then they miraculously began to function again, putting out huge amounts of urine. And surprisingly, Cameron suffered no seizures as one might expect after a brain is oxygen-deprived. Her muscle tone was decreased for a day or so, then it, too, normalized. We made her parents aware of everything that was happening to their third child and second girl. My fellow neonatologists and I had numerous daily conversations with them about her progress, her setbacks, the likelihood of poor overall outcome, and the possibility of *cerebral palsy* or mental retardation, and other lifelong problems usually due to oxygen deprivation. There always remained, however, that one ray of hope.

Cameron didn't have the two classic signs of oxygen-deprived brain damage: seizures or prolonged poor responsiveness. Once it was apparent that Cameron would survive, her parents' concern over life-and-death issues turned to questioning why it all had happened to their baby in the first place. Psychic energy goes only so far. Parents can't agonize over the life-and-death status of their child and simultaneously look to place blame. Under extreme duress, the human brain needs to focus its energy in one direction at a time. Human nature sets priorities, and usually chooses the clinical status of the baby over the culpability of certain individuals.

Occasionally parents choose from the outset to place blame on the doctors, the nursing staff, or the hospital instead of dealing with the critical nature of their child's illness. They don't want to hear about the ongoing status of their infant's health; they just want to know why and who is responsible. Surely someone did something wrong; otherwise their baby would not be in such a dire predicament. Medical care is supposed to be perfect, isn't it? The doctor should have known that this might happen. He or she should have been more careful and taken steps to prevent any complications.

How does the attending neonatologist handle such questions? How does one respond if one suspects or even knows that the family might be correct in their suspicions that their baby is suffering because someone wasn't careful, had deficient knowledge, poor skills, was lazy, circumvented the rules, or committed an unintentional error? Or perhaps the reason was due to some weak hospital policy or a specific protocol in place that allowed the error to occur, because the hospital hadn't provided adequate checks and balances.

Up until quite recently the unwritten rule was to try to absent one's self when the questions were asked, and to be vague in one's responses if responses were unavoidable. We understood that we were never to admit that something had gone wrong, never to acknowledge that any doctor, nurse, or hospital, especially our own, had made a mistake. Now, in the contemporary twenty-first-century climate of truth-and-error prevention, denial and evasion are not only passé, but full disclosure for errors is considered the better, healthier trend. Simply state the truth without pointing fingers. Admit any errors, and try to right them as best as possible. The child's suffering or injury can't be undone. Medical literature tells us that what most families desire is an honest answer as to what happened and why. Ultimately they seek assurance that what happened to their loved one won't happen in the future to anyone else's loved one. That doesn't mean they won't file a malpractice suit to recover damages. However, it may mean that some will be less angry, and less angry people are less likely to sue.

But what if it isn't my own mistake, but rather another physician's, another nurse's, or another hospital's error that caused or contributed to the infant's problems? Perhaps the referring obstetrician made a bad call? Or a hospital's nurses failed to alert a doctor when the fetal monitor indicated trouble? Or maybe the anesthesiologist neglected to suction out meconium before proceeding with artificial ventilation? Perhaps financial restraints led to a lack of adequate training or equipment at the small community hospital? In those blameworthy situations, how does one answer parents who are grieving the loss of normalcy for their baby?

It's one thing to admit one's own mistakes. We must all strive to be accountable for our own actions. But how can we honestly address another's possible errors without appearing to place blame squarely on another individual or facility? The response I find best for me is two-pronged. If the question is about obstetrical management, I explain that I'm a neonatologist, not an obstetrician. That might sound like a cop-out, but it happens to be the truth. As neonatologists we have some fundamental knowledge about obstetrics, but we lack the expertise of obstetricians. We certainly could not serve as expert witnesses for obstetrical management in depositions or in court.

I encourage the family to meet with the obstetrician to discuss what might have gone wrong during the pregnancy and delivery. The family must be proactive in their search for answers. I may call the obstetrician to alert him that the family has concerns about the care he's provided. We may discuss the events of labor and delivery. I encourage him to sit down with the family and go over the events truthfully and in detail. If there really seems to be malpractice involved, a skilled plaintiff's attorney will attempt to prove it, with experts to buttress his points, regardless of what explanation the defendant doctor has concocted for the family. If the infant's birth took place in another hospital, I simply say that I wasn't there, and without first-hand knowledge I can't address concerns about care. In such a case I also encourage the family to talk with the obstetrician, pediatrician, administrator, or risk manager of the birth hospital. Then I alert the pediatrician or obstetrician of the other hospital of a potential malpractice suit and advise the doctor that if he or she ignores the family's concerns, or offers answers that are clearly not true, a lawsuit is more likely than if all questions are answered in an honest manner. And if some actions of the hospital were inappropriate and the care rendered could have been better, I may be bold enough to suggest that risk management consider a quality improvement program addressing the shortcoming.

Ideally our error rate in the health care industry should be zero. Unfortunately, it isn't. When we make mistakes, we must learn from them, so they don't happen again to another patient. In that same vein, if one of my colleagues feels that care rendered at a referring hospital, prior to transport to our facility, could have been better, a phone call is made doctor-to-doctor to discuss the details and alternatives to the treatment provided. We used to document our critique of care in transported infants with a confidential letter to the referring physician as part of our transport peer-review program. Several years ago we stopped that practice for fear of such letters falling into the wrong hands.

As Cameron's condition improved and it became apparent that she would survive, her family began to question the events surrounding their daughter's birth and transfer. They had seen Cameron in the delivery room. She hadn't looked wonderful, but she surely hadn't looked like a blue bloated monster. Her *Apgar scores* were two and seven at one and five minutes respectively, suggesting that she was in decent condition by five minutes of life. A one-minute Apgar score correlates with the immediate condition of the baby at birth. The five-minute score shows the skill of the resuscitator, and also reflects events prior to birth going back more than a few minutes. So scores of two and seven suggest some compromise at birth that was short-lived, as well as the presence of a skilled operator attending the baby. Alternatively, the scores were overly generous, suggesting that the person assigning the Apgar scores had overestimated them. This could have been done in order to make the baby seem less ill than she had actually been at birth, or more likely, the scorer did the best he or she could do remembering the infant's condition ten or fifteen minutes after the fact. Although Apgar scores are supposed to be done in real time, events of deliveries sometimes delay the scoring until after the dust settles.

I tried to relate to her family what had happened to Cameron without passing judgment on events I hadn't seen. Although I suspected that the anesthesiologist hadn't suctioned the infant, I didn't say that specifically. Although I was fairly sure that he had failed to recognize the problem of meconium clogging the infant's *endotracheal tube*, and that his anesthesia team had failed to turn on the oxygen in the nursery, I didn't offer those explanations. And the fact that the anesthesiologist had left the infant in the nursery and had disappeared before the team arrived went unsaid. I hadn't been there, and could not say for sure exactly what had occurred. With time, Cameron's family pieced the events together and later, with the aid of a knowledgeable personal injury lawyer and expert witnesses, realized that the care rendered to Cameron hadn't been optimal.

The Lawsuit

Cameron spent four weeks in the hospital. At discharge she appeared to be in good condition, albeit with a significant question mark regarding her future. Based on her hospital course, we knew that she remained at high risk for the development of neurological and developmental complications. Unfortunately, by six months of age she began to show signs of *spastic quadriplegia*, a severe form of cerebral palsy.[5] We knew that, as she grew, she would need special devices and human assistance to aid her in the activities of daily living. She would also need physical, occupational, and speech therapy, as well as special education classes. Cameron might never be able to function entirely independently. Some degree of supervision and assistance could be required even in adulthood. Her lifespan, however, would probably be normal.

When Cameron turned two years old, her family filed a multimillion dollar malpractice suit against many players: Remington Hospital, where Cameron had been born; the obstetrician, Dr. Sage; and the anesthesiologist, Dr. Knight. Also included in the lawsuit was the hapless pediatrician, Dr. Boucher, who hadn't even laid hands on the infant until after hospital discharge! The C family didn't sue any of the neonatologists who shared in the care of their infant, the neonatal transport team, Pine Grove Hospital, or any of its staff. We were the good guys in the tall white hats, who galloped in on white horses, scooped up their baby, and saved her life. It's great to be a hero safe and secure in the towers of the tertiary center, a gallant knight who cleans up other health care professionals' messes, and blessed to be clothed in shining armor capable of deflecting the arrows and javelins of malpractice suits.

As the initial treating physician, I was subpoenaed to give a deposition as to the facts of the case as I knew them. Standard operating procedure dictated that the testifying physician's malpractice insurance company provide an attorney for a physician witness. Most malpractice carriers would not permit physicians to talk informally with a plaintiff's attorney, even if the physician was merely a party to the events surrounding the lawsuit and wasn't actually being sued. Insurance companies feared that the testifying physician might say something self-incriminating, whereupon the plaintiff's attorney could jump at the chance to enjoin that physician in the lawsuit, hence the need for having a lawyer present.

Mr. Blackstone, a short, soft-spoken, middle-aged man, attired in the requisite dark pin-striped suit, was my appointed attorney. I met with him the night before my deposition so that we could go over the facts surrounding Cameron's birth and resuscitation in intricate and painful detail.

After exchanging pleasantries, Mr. Blackstone opened: "Dr. Sacks, is there is anything that you or your staff at Pine Grove might have done that could have contributed to Cameron's disability? I need to be sure about that before the depositions begin."

Mr. Blackstone's question didn't surprise me. I had done a few chart reviews for defense attorneys. I had recently reviewed Cameron's entire hospital chart in preparation for my deposition. I assured Mr. Blackstone that neither Pine Grove's staff nor any of the neonatologists had done anything wrong. No omissions of care or commissions of errors that contributed to her less than perfect outcome had jumped out at me from the pages of Cameron's chart. The following afternoon I showed up at the specified time at the board room of Remington Hospital for my deposition. This wasn't my first deposition, so I wasn't too nervous. The preparatory meeting with Mr. Blackstone had also lowered my anxiety level considerably. After knocking on the closed door, I cautiously entered the room, which was crowded with parties to the lawsuit and their attorneys. Present were Mr. and Mrs. C and their two attorneys, as well as the defendants: the obstetrician, the anesthesiologist, and the pediatrician, each with his respective attorney, the Remington Hospital attorney, the court reporter, and of course, Mr. Blackstone.

Mr. Blackstone immediately stood up. "Gentlemen and ladies, would you allow me a few minutes' recess to confer with my client, please?" He excused himself from the room and led me to an armchair in the adjacent room. "Please sit down, Dr. Sacks. I have something to tell you before we begin your testimony."

I was clueless. What did he need to tell me? Hadn't we gone over the facts of the case, ad nauseum, and the role I had played in salvaging Cameron's life that fateful evening and in her subsequent care? Momentarily, I worried that maybe I should not have tried so hard to save her. That's always a concern when a baby has a prolonged resuscitation. Do we do a baby such as Cameron a good deed by saving him or her, or have we condemned them to lives of suffering and hardship secondary to severe handicaps? It's the million dollar question to which the answer can be known only in retrospect. The answer is subjective as well. Who is entitled to determine how much disability renders the decision to save a life the wrong decision?

One of my former neonatal fellows, now a prominent neonatologist practicing in our nation's capital, used to have twin sayings that he would preach to the pediatric residents. Regarding neonatal resuscitation Stan would opine, "When in doubt, go full out," and "Every baby deserves at least one well-run, well-coordinated resuscitation attempt." Simplistic, sarcastic, caustic maybe, but true. Those are the unwritten rules under which we neonatologists operate.

No, the fact that Cameron survived could not be the issue that Mr. Blackstone wanted to discuss. The C family had always acted grateful to me and the entire staff for all the efforts we put into saving their child. Whether saving her was a good move or not could not be the question. Besides, wrongful life suits are unpopular, especially in the South.

I thought back again over Cameron's hospital course. Considering her degree of illness, there were no major mistakes on our part. She didn't end up with chronic lung disease, as do some infants with meconium aspiration. There had been no neurological treatment she should have received but hadn't. My mind raced back over her hospital stay for some small but significant detail I had failed to remember on the first go-around.

Mr. Blackstone continued: "Dr. Sacks, Dr. Knight, the anesthesiologist, gave his deposition yesterday afternoon and this morning. He told us that he called you from the delivery room . . ."

"Truthfully, I can't remember if it was Dr. Knight or the OB, Dr. Sage," I interjected. I have a lifelong bad habit of interrupting, not letting others finish their thoughts. Sometimes I even finish their sentences for them. "You know, I don't work with either of them very much since they practice only at Remington, so I don't recognize their voices. Yes, I guess it could have been Dr. Knight rather than the obstetrician."

"Dr. Sacks, Dr. Knight finished his deposition this morning." Mr. Blackstone was cool and collected. He showed no signs of excitement or distress. He might as well have been discussing the fine weather we'd been having that past week. "He went on for over five hours. As you can imagine, his testimony in response to questions was very detailed. At one point he told Mr. Bailey, the C family's attorney, that he had spoken to you after Cameron was born . . ."

Where is this leading? I wondered.

". . . and that he had asked you—no, he claims he begged you—to come over to Remington Hospital immediately to assume care of the baby. He said you had flat out refused to come and help him manage this sick infant."

The blood rushed to my face. My heart sank into the pit of my stomach. I was offended to the core. Suddenly my neck was wet with nervous sweat and I felt queasy. Had I been transported into a parallel universe? I stared at Mr. Blackstone in disbelief.

"He actually said that? Dr. Knight accused me of refusing to come to help?" My heart was pounding.

"Yes, he did."

"I can't believe he said that." I was indignant. "That's not true! That's one hundred percent false! I even offered to zip over there, and he declined my help, saying it wouldn't be necessary."

"I know, Dr. Sacks. I know." Blackstone was empathetic.

I sighed, drew a deep breath, and adjusted the scarf around my neck. I tried to remain calm, but could not. How could my colleague have told such an egregious falsehood about me? What could I do about it? How could I set the record straight? A deposition is a legal record, and it stated in black and white that I had refused to help a colleague. Worse, I refused to help a sick baby! And it was written down in an official document!

"First of all, even if I was the biggest SOB on the planet, it would be just plain stupid to refuse to take care of a sick patient who urgently needed my help. Physicians who do that certainly set themselves up for a lawsuit, and who in their right mind would do that?" Yet, I thought, ironically, *That's exactly where I might be now, isn't it?*

"Secondly, Mr. Blackstone, anyone who has worked with me knows I'd never, ever knowingly place a baby's life or health in jeopardy like that. It's not in my personal nature. Sure, I make mistakes in judgment like the rest of the doctors on this planet. But this wasn't a judgment call. As Dr. Knight tells it, his conversation was a call for help. The request he claims to have made would not have been unreasonable. I'd never have refused such a request. I'm a goody two-shoes. I don't know how to say no even when I think the request lacks validity." I took another deep breath and swallowed hard. My heart was racing. I hated confrontation. But protecting my good name and reputation has always been important to me. It is an issue worth fighting for.

"The man is lying! I don't understand. Why would he do that to me?" By then I was close to tears, and crying wasn't exactly professional behavior. And I was angry as well. My sense of fair play had suffered a challenging blow. My integrity had been publicly questioned during Dr. Knight's deposition, and I hadn't even been there to defend myself and no one else had been there to defend me either. An official transcript clearly stated that I had refused to come over to Remington to help and, therefore, that what had happened to Cameron must have been my fault, or at least partially my fault. The testimony had been taken and sworn to, and after the deposition was signed, the false documents would be filed for posterity.

Mr. Blackstone didn't answer my question about Dr. Knight's motivation, which I had now asked twice. Perhaps because doctors have held themselves out as gods, the public holds the opinion that doctors have a higher standard of personal ethics than the average man. Or maybe we as doctors, playing God with people's lives, ought be held to a higher moral and ethical standard. Although I'd like to believe that physicians as a group have very high ethical standards, both at the bedside and away from the bedside, perhaps that's Pollyanna thinking. Like every other profession, medicine certainly has its rotten apples. Twenty years after the events I have described, I had the privilege and honor of serving as president of the more than six-hundred members of the medical staff at Pine Grove Hospital. In terms of compliance with the mores of day-to-day dealings with patients and staff, following the rules of patient safety, and demonstrating collaborative conduct with each other and the rest of the health care team, I found that doctors' behavior fell into the famous bell-shaped curve. Almost daily my office received a complaint about less-than-outstanding physician behavior.

My deposition in the C case lasted three hours. Mr. Bailey, the plaintiff's lead attorney, asked me for my recollection of that evening when Cameron entered this world. He didn't specifically ask me to refute Dr. Knight's rendition of the events. Nor did Dr. Knight's attorney ask me specifically why I had refused to come to the hospital as his client had claimed. I guess he didn't want me to call Dr. Knight a lying bastard. He must have known that his doctor-client was lying, but didn't want to call specific attention to it by having me show righteous indignation. As my deposition was about to conclude, Mr. Blackstone requested the addition of some specific wording to the official transcript that would show Dr. Knight had lied without actually stating so. I suppose lawyers want documentation to take a higher ground when mud is being or has been thrown.

"Mr. Bailey, it is my understanding that you have not, and don't have any intention of joining my client, Dr. Sacks, in this lawsuit. Is that correct?" Mr. Blackstone wanted to be certain that Mr. Bailey didn't believe Dr. Knight. If Mr. Bailey did, it would've been logical to name me in the lawsuit. Hell, I'd be the biggest culprit of all. I had been painted in the light of having refused to help a dying baby. Who could possibly bear a larger burden of guilt?

"You are correct, sir. Dr. Sacks is not part of this lawsuit, and will not be added at any time." Dr. Knight had slung mud at me, but his own lawyer and mine had made sure that I hadn't returned fire, and that he looked all the more foolish. I'd have liked to have sued Dr. Knight for his having maligned my professionalism and ethics. But Mr. Blackstone explained to me that depositions are special places in which people can lie and sometimes get away with it. He explained that since no one believed Dr. Knight and that therefore nothing would come of his lie, there would be no professional or financial damage to me, and therefore no basis for suing.

Cameron's lawsuit was settled out of court for an annuity of mega millions against the hospital, the obstetrician, and the anesthesiologist.

I never saw the family or the child again. Dr. Boucher, the pediatrician who assumed care only after Cameron was discharged from the hospital, was ultimately dismissed from the lawsuit. He was so distressed by the experience of being accused of malpractice that he took early retirement from active pediatric practice. Dr. Sage, the obstetrician, went on to practice successfully for another twenty years without a single lawsuit.

Dr. Knight, who must have been only a few years out of residency training at the time of Cameron's birth, moved on to another hospital in the Midwest soon after the settlement. I like to think he was too embarrassed by his bald-faced lie about me to continue appearing in the halls of the labor and delivery suite where we might meet. Later I found out that in the few weeks after Cameron's birth, well before the lawsuit was filed, Dr. Knight attempted to get labor and delivery nurses, as well as those in the special care nursery who were involved in Cameron's care, to sign affidavits asserting that the care he rendered had been exemplary. To a man (well, to a woman, actually) they had all refused.

When last examined at age three in the developmental clinic by my colleagues, Cameron showed severe physical handicaps, but appeared to have near-normal intelligence. As a direct result of Cameron's disastrous birth and botched resuscitation, my partners and I requested that Pine Grove's CEO, Keith Ashford, permit us to enjoy full privileges at Remington. With full privileges we could attend deliveries, as well as manage slightly ill infants in the *Level II* nursery there. We could do a lot of good work and possibly prevent future scenarios like Cameron's. Mr. Ashford, in his typical I-am-in-control fashion, refused to consider our request. Remington Hospital, badly burned in reputation and pocketbook by Cameron's misfortune, countered by making overtures toward hiring its own neonatologist. A separate neonatal service at Remington, even one staffed by a solo practitioner, would surely have siphoned business away from Pine Grove, especially patients with good insurance coverage.

My partners and I campaigned for our request by warning Mr. Ashford that Remington would succeed in its attempt to hire its own neonatologist. Actually this scenario was unlikely, given Remington's volume of business and the fact that no sane neonatologist would agree to be the only one, meaning that he or she would have to be on call twenty-four hours a day, seven days a week. Our group could not and would not cross cover with anyone Remington hired. The impasse created by Mr. Ashford was untenable. We applied for full privileges at Remington in direct disobedience of Mr. Ashford's edict. Essentially we called Mr. Ashford's (and I suppose Pine Grove Hospital Board's) bluff. We were in breach of contract, albeit for a noble cause. Ashford could have fired the three of us, but he didn't. We were granted full privileges at Remington Hospital and from that time forward we attended all complex and high-risk deliveries there.

At least some good resulted from Cameron's disaster.

1. Textbooks of the past tell us that ten to twenty percent of newborns pass meconium stool in utero before they are born. After 2000 the incidence fell markedly, since twenty-first-century obstetricians don't permit women to go more than one week post date. After forty-one weeks, there is an increased incidence of stillbirth and other problems—like meconium passage—as the placenta runs out of steam and its ability to sustain its life-supportive functions diminishes.

2. The consistency of the final product depends on three factors: the relative amount of meconium that was passed, the volume of the fluid with which it mixes, and the length of time the meconium has been present in the amniotic fluid. Thin meconium is thought to be less of a threat to fetal well-being than thick meconium. If meconium is present in the amniotic fluid when membranes rupture, some obstetricians infuse the uterus with saline to wash out or dilute the meconium. It used to be thought that such action led to a lower incidence of meconium aspiration and fetal distress. By the end of the 1990's that theory had also fallen by the wayside although the practice continued.

3. Q.E.D. is Latin for *quid est demonstrandum*, which means "which was to be shown," a phrase from mathematics, especially trigonometry.

4. Meconium plugs airways with a ball-valve mechanism. It may let air in, but blocks its exit on expiration. The air sac gets larger and larger until it bursts.

5. Spastic quadriplegia results from an injury to the motor cortex of the brain. The affected infant develops tightness—spasticity of both arms and legs, usually legs more affected than arms. He has trouble with gross

and fine motor skills. In its mildest form, the patient is clumsy and may walk on his toes. Spastic quadriplegia can also affect speech. In its most severe form the patient develops contractures and is confined to a wheel-chair. It can also be associated with mental impairment of various degrees.

7

Elijah

A Difficult Beginning

"Do you believe in miracles? Well, do you, doctor?" The inquiry was not said in a childish or merely probative manner. The question was a definite challenge, a defiant question from the lips of an angry forty-three-year-old grandfather. If this had been a movie, the music would have changed to a wartime theme. The trumpets would have blasted. Background music would have let us know that the theology-versus-medicine jousting contest was about to begin on the tiled battlefield of the neonatal unit.

A small group of family and health care professionals were seated in comfortable sofas and chairs around a wooden coffee table in the neonatal conference room. There were seven of us in all. Tarnisha K was the chubby sweat-suited teenaged mother, now one week postpartum. Her hair was fixed in one of the wildest Afros I had ever seen. Side by side sat my patient's maternal grandmother and her elderly mother, the baby's maternal great-grandmother. The well-groomed grandmother looked overwhelmed. The baby's great-grandmother fulfilled my white man's vision of the southern African-American family matriarch, minus the Jackie Kennedy pillbox hat: tailored light blue suit, white silk blouse, sensible low-heeled shoes with matching handbag. Great-grandmother could have come directly from Wednesday night church services. Number four was the blue-collar maternal grandfather whose hands were clean but calloused. He appeared to be the person in charge in this group. Numbers five and six were Katie, our veteran social worker, who had heard it all more than once, and Beth, the infant's bedside nurse. I was number seven, the neonatologist in charge of the baby's care. The FOB (neonatal shorthand for father of the baby) was conspicuously absent, as he had been from day one. I did not believe that the teenage mother knew who the father was. Or perhaps she did, but didn't want to involve him. Or maybe he himself didn't want the responsibilities of fatherhood. Suffice it to say, we were informed on the day of admission that the FOB would not be visiting or permitted to get information about the baby.

As far as the family knew, they were meeting with me for an update on the precarious condition of their son, grandson, and great-grandson Elijah. Ah, what's in a name? I wonder, was it selected by his mom during pregnancy? That's doubtful. More likely, it was given to him after the circumstances of his birth by a family member familiar with Biblical prophecy. Elijah the Prophet's return to earth will presage the coming (or Second Coming, depending on one's religious orientation) of the Messiah. I wonder who chose it?

My agenda—unknown to the family but clear to Katie and Beth— was to introduce to the family two uncomfortable subjects: a do-not-resuscitate order (DNR) for Elijah and/or possible withdrawal of life support.

Tarnisha K, Elijah's mother, was a moderately obese adolescent who successfully hid her pregnancy from her parents until the day she delivered. Just two days before she gave birth, Tarnisha found out for certain from the clinic that she was pregnant. Although Tarnisha may have revealed her expectant status to friends, she did not tell anyone in her immediate family. On the evening of Elijah's birth, Tarnisha complained of severe stomach pains. Her mother ascertained that she had no fever, nausea, vomiting, or diarrhea.

"Tarnisha, what's wrong with you, baby? You look like you're hurtin' bad," she asked.

Mrs. K, Tarnisha's mother, was really concerned. Tarnisha was normally not a complainer. However, she was so uncomfortable that Mrs. K believed that something was seriously amiss with her oldest child's health. *Could be appendicitis*, she thought. Tarnisha did not want to go to the hospital, but over her objections her parents rushed her to their local community hospital emergency room. I did not know the specific health history information that the emergency department (ED) triage nurse requested from Tarnisha, but the teenager did not reveal to the triage nurse that she might be in labor. Tarnisha did not even tell the nurse that she was in the family way. All women of childbearing age are presumed pregnant in the ED until proven otherwise, and therefore are usually asked, "Any chance you might be pregnant, dear?" Therefore, Tarnisha probably lied about not being pregnant. Without an examination, as far as the hospital staff knew, Tarnisha was just another victim of the bad stomach virus that was making the rounds of kids and grown-ups alike, or maybe early appendicitis. I supposed a pregnancy test was sent off to the lab, just to be sure. That would be standard operating procedure. Despite her pain and discomfort, Tarnish waited patiently and silently on a hard chair in the ED on that busy Saturday evening.

For three hours she waited her turn to be seen. One has to wonder what thoughts were going through her mind. Even not having ever had a baby before, she must have intuitively suspected she was in labor. Pregnancy at term plus bad belly pain usually equals labor, even to first-timers. Wasn't she worried about the baby? If not the baby, then wasn't she concerned at least about herself? Was she punishing herself by remaining silent and enduring her pain? After all, the good book says that Eve's punishment for consuming the apple is to bring forth children in pain. Was she hoping something would happen to her baby and it would be stillborn? That would be one solution to her problem. She couldn't really have been in denial, could she?

Freshman year in college my mother greeted me on my arrival home from class one winter evening with, "You'll never guess who just had a baby!"

I didn't know anyone who was pregnant at the time. "Okay, I give up, who had a baby?" To tell the truth, I really wasn't particularly interested. But Mom was always ready to pass on the latest gossip.

"Sally Demcrest had a baby last night. She told Jack that she thought she had appendicitis. He took her to Einstein Center with appendicitis and she had a little girl two hours later. What a *shanda!*"[1]

Poor Mr. Demcrest. The sordid details came to light a few days later. The family doctor met them that snowy February night in the ED. Jack Demcrest waited anxiously while his youngest daughter was examined. Emerging from the cubicle where he had just examined Sally, the good doctor announced to Mr. Demcrest, "Congratulations, sir, you're going to be a grandfather."

A grandfather? Jack was shocked and not overly pleased. In that unenlightened age of the mid 1960's, births out of wedlock to middle class eighteen-year-old white girls were still an embarrassment.

"So, Doc, when is she due?" Jack asked when the blessed event was going to occur, meaning what month—in the spring or summer? Just how far along in pregnancy was his unmarried daughter?

"Tonight," the doctor replied. I wonder if he smiled. A short time later, five-and-a-half-pound Sarah Rose entered the world by spontaneous vaginal delivery. Sally and the baby's father, David, were married by a rabbi in Sally's hospital room the next day. The marriage lasted only six months, but legitimized little Sarah Rose. That legitimization didn't curtail the neighborhood *yentas*.[2]

Sally, who was five feet and four inches tall and of medium build, had hidden a full-term pregnancy from her parents by wearing bulky clothes. Neighbors had even observed her shoveling snow from the walk outside her home two weeks previously. That hidden pregnancy occurred over forty years ago. Some communications which occur—or don't occur— between a teenager and her family haven't changed in decades.

When Tarnisha was finally examined, the ED doctor discovered that the infant's head was crowning! Too late he realized that not only was Tarnisha in labor, but delivery was imminent; there was no time for transfer to labor and delivery. Tarnisha delivered her firstborn son in the ED under barely controlled and definitely nonsterile conditions. The baby was a large-term infant. He was floppy and coated with a thick green, slimy covering that resembled pea soup. He was coated with *meconium*, fetal stool. Judging from the deeply meconium-stained skin and nails of the baby, the meconium had obviously been in the fluid for a long time, hours to days.

This situation was a neonatal emergency. Tarnisha's newly born, meconium-covered infant was not moving. He was not breathing either. The ensuing ED resuscitation was chaotic. Experienced ED personnel are comfortable dealing with heart attacks in old men and strokes in elderly women. They routinely patch up gunshot victims. With great dexterity, knowing that every second counts, they rapidly assess victims of motorcycle wrecks. They are skilled at reviving gang bangers after drug overdoses. But they are not used to birthing babies. Babies are born in labor and delivery!

Once the nature of Tarnisha's distress was painfully clear to all concerned, the staff was challenged to locate the proper equipment. Although there was an emergency childbirth kit available, the ED personnel did not have immediate access to a warmer bed to prevent heat loss in the newborn. There was an emergency respiratory box and a neonatal drug box in the ED as well, but who remembered where it was? They knew they must follow specific neonatal resuscitation guidelines, which maybe they once knew but never before had the necessity to use. The guidelines were similar to, but not identical with, the recommendations for pediatric and adult resuscitation. Could they recall the guidelines?

The ED team called immediately for emergency assistance from the nursery staff. Unfortunately the hospital birthing center and nursery areas were on the other side of the hospital complex. Skilled help did not arrive until ten minutes after the birth of Tarnisha's baby. In their panic the ED team forgot the basics: dry the baby off and try to keep it warm. When he finally reached the nursery, Elijah was ice-cold, with a temperature of ninety-two degrees.

Formal resuscitation guidelines for newborns were first published by the American Heart Association and American Academy of Pediatrics in

1985 and have been updated four times.[3] Many recommendations have changed over the years, but one of the rules for providing assisted breathing in the presence of meconium has not. If meconium is present and the infant isn't breathing, the doctor must insert a tube into the baby's windpipe to suction out any meconium that is present in the trachea *before* providing bag-and-mask resuscitation. To do otherwise may drive the meconium, thick or thin, down into the airways. Meconium is toxic to the lungs, causing a condition called *meconium aspiration syndrome.*[4] Its severity ranges from mild disease in which the infant simply breathes too fast, to moderate disease with a requirement for oxygen and/or a ventilator, to lung problems so severe that the infant requires a *high frequency jet ventilator* with *inhaled nitric oxide (iNO)* therapy. Some affected infants wind up needing up to two weeks on a heart-lung bypass machine (ECMO). Even today in the twenty-first century, there is a significant mortality rate for severe meconium aspiration syndrome.

Back to the ED. Just-born Elijah was not breathing and had a low heart rate. The ED team administered cardiac massage, positive pressure ventilation, and two doses of *adrenalin* to raise his heart rate into the normal range. But his airway was not suctioned to remove the meconium. The result of Elijah's resuscitation under less than optimal conditions was predictable. His Apgar scores were 1, 1, 3, and 3 at one, five, ten, and fifteen minutes of life respectively. A score of 3 or less at ten minutes augurs poorly for survival and normal development. The longer the score remains three or less, the worse the child's prognosis. Elijah ended up with lots of meconium in his lungs. It could have been aspirated into his lungs minutes or even hours before birth. It might have been introduced at the hands of the ED docs who gave positive pressure ventilation before sucking out meconium from his trachea. It was impossible to know which—or both—scenarios occurred. Elijah also suffered from oxygen deprivation during the final stage of his labor and /or immediately postnatally. Since the labor wasn't monitored—one cannot monitor a labor one doesn't know is in progress—we couldn't be sure when the problem started.

While our transport team was in route to the hospital to pick him up, Elijah began to have seizures, indicating that his brain had been deprived of oxygen. His arms and legs shook rhythmically; his eyes blinked and deviated to the left. During these episodes his heart rate and oxygen level fell. A loading dose of phenobarbital quieted his seizure activity temporarily. The transport team followed protocol and administered *intravenous* saline to try to increase his blood pressure into the normal range. When this maneuver was unsuccessful, they began an infusion of *dopamine*, a cardiac stimulant that increases both heart rate and blood pressure. Elijah remained on maximal ventilator settings during transport. His admission diagnoses were severe meconium aspiration, cardiogenic shock, and seizures.

A Difficult End

After Elijah was admitted to our NICU, it was apparent that he had additional problems affecting multiple organ systems. Lack of oxygen occurring in utero or shortly after birth was responsible for the damage we saw in his major organ systems. Elijah's heart muscle had been injured from inadequate oxygen delivery. His heart was not able to pump efficiently to maintain an oxygen supply to his vital organs. Despite infusion of cardiac drugs, his blood pressure remained dangerously low. Elijah moved neither spontaneously nor in response to touch or deep pain. Brushing his corneas with a sterile cotton swab did not elicit a protective blink. He did not try to breathe when we momentarily disconnected him from the ventilator. Persistent seizures and global depression of nervous function told us that Elijah's central nervous system had suffered a severe, most likely irreversible insult. Elevated liver enzymes indicated that his hepatic system also suffered a hit; its injured cells poured out enzymes into his circulation. His kidneys failed. They made no urine for twenty-four hours. Within two days of delivery bloody stools filled his diaper, a manifestation of injury to his bowel as well. His platelet count was low and he oozed blood from needle-puncture sites.

For the first four days of life Elijah's condition remained precarious. He hovered on that fine line between life and death. Then, thanks to his doctors' and nurses' skills, modern technology, fresh frozen plasma, blood and platelet transfusions, and Heaven's protection (according to his family) his many problems began to resolve, slowly, one by one. By a week of age he no longer required cardiac drugs, his blood clotted normally, and his liver enzymes had returned to baseline values. His bowel wall stopped bleeding so he no longer passed bloody stools. The baby no longer required additional oxygen, although he remained ventilator dependent. Elijah had little to no spontaneous respiratory effort. Most likely his brain was still swollen in reaction to the previous lack of oxygen. Alternatively his brain stem (which controls respiration) had been so damaged that it no longer sent signals via his *phrenic nerve* to his diaphragm telling it to contract, to take another breath. Anticonvulsant medication kept his seizures from recurring. His EEG (brain wave test) did not show any more electrical seizure activity. All was not well cerebrally, however. The most recent EEG had shown burst suppression, an ominous pattern. Frenzied volleys of abnormal brainwaves lasting a few seconds were followed by a period of flat lines indicating lack of brain activity. Developmental studies in infants with burst suppression patterns uniformly demonstrate poor outcome. The result for most children with burst suppression EEG pattern is death or survival in a vegetative or near-vegetative state. The occasional survivor does better—surviving with severe *cerebral palsy* and profound intellectual impairment.

This stage in Elijah's recovery presented a window of opportunity for the family to make the most difficult, yet most important, decision they would ever be asked to make. Several days had passed since the trauma of finding out that their hope for a perfect child had evaporated. Mother and grandparents have had some time to grieve the loss of that perfect child. They may not have understood the grief process, but grieving was what they had been doing, simultaneously with hoping and praying for Elijah's recovery. Our expectation as health care professionals was that they now surrender the dreams they held for him. What's done is done, and the sooner they recognized that fact, the sooner we could plan for Elijah's future, or lack of future. It seemed so clear to us, so rational, we who have seen a hundred Elijahs in our careers. We understood the hopelessness of his situation; why couldn't they? They saw his unresponsiveness. Surely they knew he wasn't acting like a normal newborn.

The dilemma the family faced at this point—the dilemma that fell to me to place squarely before them—was an awful choice: allow Elijah's natural death by discontinuing heroic care, or persist with supportive therapy that couldn't reverse the damage that had occurred. Continued treatment if successful would produce a severely disabled survivor with a shortened life span, perhaps even a child that would remain in a vegetative state. Or Elijah might die in spite of our technology and drugs. Continued treatment would not reverse the damage. The statistics on babies like Tarnisha's son were real. The statistics were cruel, but I hadn't made them up. I wished they were not so. But they were, and I was only the messenger.

Elijah was not brain dead. There are specific detailed criteria required to make that diagnosis, and it is rare that a neonate ever meets those criteria. But no amount of physical therapy or medication was going to restore his brain to anything close to its pristine healthy condition. Statistics tell us that newborns who are ventilator dependent at this postnatal stage because of brain (rather than lung) issues, may not ever breathe on their own no matter how much time we allow them on the ventilator. Even if they recover respiratory function, they will have problems with other brainstem functions, such as coordination of suck-and-swallow. At the minimum, infants like Elijah will need placement of a feeding tube to provide nutrition. Many of these babies will also not even be able to swallow their own secretions. The surgeons will have to place a *tracheostomy* so that Elijah does not drown in his own saliva, or aspirate his tube feedings into his lungs. Some babies like Elijah, ventilator dependent at a week of age due to brain damage, never come off the ventilator on their own. The decision of whether to withdraw support is merely postponed to a later date, when it may be even more difficult for the family to decide what is in the best interest of their baby and what they should do.

Elijah had reached a critical turning point in his short life. All his organs, save his brain, had recovered to the point of normal lab values. But even when his brain swelling would decrease further, his higher cerebral function would remain minimal. I had asked the family to join me in the conference room so that I could attempt to explain in layman's terms the physiology of what had occurred. To make an informed decision, they must understand Elijah's poor prognosis for life and the nil prognosis for anything resembling normal development. These devastating facts were not new information for them. The sad saga of what happened to Elijah at birth and the bleak future he faced had been reiterated to them at least once daily since admission by multiple physicians and nurses, although it had always been softened with the caveat, "I'm concerned that" or "I'm worried because." Devastated parents need repetition and time to absorb all the bad news. No doctor had yet declared dead the hope that Elijah would experience a total recovery of his physical and neurological health. Unfortunately, pronouncing that hope dead was my job that afternoon.

In retrospect, I should have known that I would not get through to this particular family. Tarnisha, sitting directly across from me, would not make eye contact with me. She never had. Emotions of fifteen-year-old mothers of sick infants run the gamut from withdrawn and quiet, ashamed, guilt ridden and despondent, to arrogant and proud of the fruits of their wombs. For some teenaged mothers, their babies are the major accomplishment of their young lives. Tarnisha was hard to figure. It was apparent that her family was totally supportive of her and the baby. If they were angry about her pregnancy or the fact that she had hidden it from them, they did not show it publicly. In exchange for emotional and financial support of her situation, she ceded to them the right to call the shots, a common scenario. Kids are old enough to have sex, to become pregnant, and to give birth, but not old enough or mature enough to make decisions for their babies, decisions that will affect their kids and themselves forever. Psychological maturity lags behind physiological maturity by several years at the minimum. The gap seems to widen each year.

I explained all of Elijah's issues in layman's terms to the K family. This discussion took thirty minutes. With great patience but without enthusiasm I started with a recitation of the positive improvement he'd shown regarding his lungs, heart, bowels, and liver. Then I dealt with the down side, the evidence of brain damage. When I persisted in my concern that Elijah's brain function would never recover, Grandfather K hit me totally out of the blue with his question about miracles: "Do you believe in miracles, Dr. Sacks?"

Miracle was a word never mentioned in my medical training, other than in the phrase, "It'll be a miracle if I pass this neuroanatomy test!" I consider myself a seriously religious and spiritual individual. I readily acknowledge that science cannot explain everything. I've seen infants survive who by all logic and reason should have died. Miracle is the only explanation for their survival. During my now-grown children's adolescence, I had numerous heated discussions with my sons about these miraculous survivors. My boys insisted that eventually science, not theology, would one day explain why some sick babies survive even if today we don't know why. I am not a stranger to discussions about the role of the Divine in patients' recoveries. I routinely place the names of seriously ill friends and relatives on the prayer list of my synagogue, and make charitable donations to speed their recoveries. I am neither unsympathetic nor antagonistic toward religious beliefs.

"Yes, Mr. K, I do believe in miracles. Every single baby in this neonatal unit is a miracle." I found myself staring at him. "Ten to twenty years ago most of them would have died. Even five years ago Elijah certainly would have died on the first day of his life. It's a miracle that most of his organs have recovered. It's a miracle that he no longer needs extra oxygen. His platelet count is normal. His liver and kidneys are working again. God made all those systems better."

Perhaps if I rephrased Elijah's condition in semitheological terms, Mr. K would understand. Perhaps he wouldn't view me as the enemy. I didn't share with him my belief that the everyday neonatal miracles I witness can be attributed to the fact that the Creator has purposely endowed human beings with intelligence and curiosity. God has nurtured in their hearts the desire to do good, and bequeathed to their egos aspirations for accomplishments, fame, and fortune, and that's why scientific research has taken us so far. God has planned well. In the future these Divine gifts will take us even further. God willing, maybe someday we would be able to treat infants like his grandson. We would be able to reverse the cerebral injury so these babies won't be condemned to a lifetime of severe handicap or early death.

"But for reasons we don't understand," I continued, "although God can make your grandchild's lungs, and heart, and kidneys better, when the brain is injured as severely as Elijah's was, God cannot make that better."

"Your God cannot make Elijah's brain better?" Tarnisha's father stared right back at me. If looks could kill, I'd be dead. And I wouldn't be passing through those pearly gates.

"No, He can't," I admitted. "My God cannot make Elijah's brain better."

"Well, Dr. Sacks, my God can! He surely can!" Thus ended the conversation, and with it any chance for the family to decide to withdraw support or even to put into place a modified Do Not Resuscitate order. However, I did bring up these unpleasant issues even knowing full well that their religious beliefs coupled with their denial of reality and distrust of me would not permit them to limit support.

Deep religious faith, regardless of the specific religion or denomination, helps families through the most trying times. If their critically ill infant dies, the parents' immediate responses fall into two categories. The typical and predictable responses that we as neonatologists witness, are sentiments such as, "It was God's will"; "Jesus called Malcolm home"; "God knows best"; "Keith isn't suffering anymore"; and "Janie is in a better place." Their faith and sectarian dogma allow them to accept their loved one's death. They imagine their precious baby among the angels, free from pain and patiently waiting for a reunion with them at some point in the distant future. With faith they are able to acknowledge their Creator's wisdom, even if they don't agree with His decision or the arbitrary outcome. They grieve, they ache, their hearts are broken; but their faith in the Deity comforts them and guides them through the lengthy healing process.

But occasionally, especially among the most devout, an infant's death shatters the parents' belief system. Prayers are only to be answered in the affirmative. By not granting their fervent supplications for their baby's recovery, God has failed them. I remember Dana, who lost her twenty-five-week premature infant after four months of a long roller-coaster course in the neonatal unit. Every day of those four months Dana sat at Lee's bedside reading to him from the Scriptures. Her own personal Bible lay open to a different psalm every night in the corner of his bed. One of the neonatal nurses and I went to Lee's funeral. The baby, dressed in a white christening gown, looked like he was asleep, resting on a blue satin blanket in a tiny white open casket.

Dana was seated on the first row of the tiny country church. As Nurse Annette and I approached to pay our condolences, Dana grabbed me by the arms: "Dr. Sacks, make Lee live again, make him live again!"

I was speechless. It looked to me like Dana turned to the doctor, not to God for her miracles. Her faith was gone. Her God had failed her, and she wasn't going to forgive him, not ever. Dana had lost far more than her precious child.

It took another two weeks to wean poor Elijah off the ventilator. As predicted by statistics and his nonbelieving doctor, he remained in a vegetative state. The nurses had to suction his mouth every half hour because he could not handle his own saliva. It pooled in his throat and obstructed his airway, and he turned blue. Ultimately Elijah required placement of both a feeding tube and a tracheostomy to ensure the safety of his care at home. Tarnisha and her mother roomed in with Elijah for three days in a patient room on the postpartum floor so they could practice their skills in caring for him. They had to learn how to operate the feeding pump, how to suction his trachea, how to change his tracheostomy tube, and how to do range-of-motion exercises to his stiffening limbs to prevent painful contractures. Insurance agreed to pay for round-the-clock nursing care at home, at least for a few weeks.

After frequent hospital readmissions, Tarnisha's son succumbed to pneumonia just before his second birthday.

Perhaps Mr. K's God consulted with mine. Together they decided what was really best for Elijah.

1. Yiddish for "shame, disgrace."
2. Yiddish for "gossips."
3. Ronald S. Bloom and Catherine Cropley, eds., *Neonatal Resuscitation Textbook* (American Academy of Pediatrics and American Heart Association, [1st ed.] 2005).
4. The viscous substance plugs up smaller airways. The bile salts in meconium deactivate naturally occurring surfactant. Without surfactant, air sacs collapse. Through its binding of zinc, meconium promotes bacterial overgrowth as well.

8

BE CAREFUL WHAT YOU WISH FOR

Do Everything For My Baby!

"No surprise, Craig, the parents, of course, say that they want everything done for their baby," Dr. Sam Feldman, on call *perinatologist*, said.

"They always do," Dr. Craig Turk, on-call neonatologist, interrupted.

"They're young. Mom was transferred in preterm labor from Clarksville. This is their first pregnancy. They don't really understand the likely outcome," continued Sam. "I sympathize with their dilemma. I can understand how they feel, especially since this is their first child. But I've got to go with my best medical judgment, which is that an operative delivery offers no advantage. So I've told the T's that I'm not going to do a cesarian section for breech presentation of their baby. Between us, the baby has a minimal chance of survival, at best." Sam paused, waiting for another response from Craig at the other end of the phone line.

"That's for sure. Please, I don't want to deal with another fetus in my NICU. Might have to change the name to FICU."[1] Craig was nothing if not blunt.

"You know, Craig, C-section just doesn't make sense to me. At twenty-three weeks I'd have to do a classical up-and-down incision on the uterus to get the baby out, and that would commit the mom to repeat sections forever and to an increased risk of uterine rupture when she gets pregnant again, plus a small but real risk of developing a placenta accreta in a subsequent pregnancy.[2] Twenty-three weeks and one day is not a viable child in my book, don't you agree?" Sam was piling up arguments to rationalize his decision.

"You're preaching to the choir, Sam. If I never resuscitate another twenty-three weeker, I'll sleep just fine with a clear conscience. But why are you calling me? You don't need my approval or opinion. Just tell your patient that we can't do anything for her baby if it's born this early." Craig was ready to end the phone conversation.

"Can't do that, Craig, my friend. At twenty-three weeks, you know very well that Mom and Dad get to decide, not you or I. When Mrs. T delivers, just do the best you can. My preference would be no super heroics despite what the family thinks they want. But, hey, it's your butt on the line once the kid is born. Why don't you go talk to her now, before she delivers? Maybe you'll have more success talking her out of demanding a full resuscitation and full ongoing maximal support. It's really a sad situation, especially for the baby. You know what kind of suffering it's in for if we go all out."

"Yep, it sure is a sad situation," replied Craig, thinking to himself, *especially in the middle of the night!*

"Believe me, Craig, I feel bad for them. They really want this child. But I don't think they have a clue about the hardship and pain this baby is going to face just because they want to 'give her a chance,' as their mantra goes. Anyway, I expect she'll deliver within the next few hours, certainly by morning. The ball's in your court, buddy. Sorry for the phone call, and even sorrier for the message."

The perinatologist, Dr. Sam Chester, transmitted this information—this warning, actually—by phone to my neonatal colleague Dr. Craig Turk at about ten o'clock in the evening. Sam didn't exactly request a neonatal consult, just sort of implied that one would be a good idea. Talk to Mom and Dad, tell them the slim-to-none chance their tiny soon-to-be-born-too-soon son or daughter has of surviving. Lay out for them the probable dismal outcome if he or she does manage to pull through. Allow them the opportunity to ask questions. Give them clarifying, honest, and straightforward answers. Paint a word-picture of what treatments, obstacles, and hardships their child will face for the next four months if it survives until discharge home. Tell them the greater than fifty percent likelihood of developing *cerebral palsy*, mental retardation, hearing loss and/or severe visual impairment, even blindness. At the least, following a consult the neonatologist won't be a stranger to them in the delivery room, and that's a good thing. Communication from doctor to patient is excellent medicine, the best medicine, and that's what really counts.

True to form, however, Dr. Turk elected not to talk with Mrs. T. Tall, good looking, even charming at times, Dr. Turk wasn't the parent-friendliest doctor on our staff. He was known, unfortunately, for his frequent gruff manner toward parents, staff, and recently even to his physician colleagues. Why didn't he just go to the patient's room, sit down at the bedside, and discuss the situation with the parents? Isn't that what a caring, kind, and thorough doctor should do? I like to think that's what I would have done. Perhaps Craig just didn't want to be bothered this late in the evening. Like most of us, he'd rather catch a few hours of sleep, knowing that he'd have to care for a very sick infant in the wee hours of the morning, unless, of course, he'd be lucky enough that the baby would not be born until after his shift ended at eight o'clock in the morning. I knew that Craig was exceptionally negative regarding tiny preterm infants and that he was acutely aware of his bias. Perhaps he feared offending the family with his negativity toward infants on the cusp of viability. It's hard to be truthful regarding the negative and still admit to some aspect of the positive. It's difficult to permit a glimmer of hope to come through without sounding like a Pollyanna or a false prophet. A third possibility, were it anyone other than Craig, was that his deep feelings of compassion might persuade him against his better judgment to err on the side of optimism rather than the pessimistic truth. The sugar coating of dismal information is a sin many of my colleagues committed regularly.

"Dr. Turk, we need you in labor room six, right now! The twenty-three-weeker is delivering." A few hours after his phone conversation with the obstetrician, the dreaded phone call from a labor and delivery nurse awakened Craig from a deep sleep in the middle of the night. Without a neonatal consult, twenty-six-year-old Laurie T delivered her fetus as a vaginal breech birth. Were the fetus more mature, even twenty-four weeks, she might have been delivered by cesarian section in order to avoid the possibility of entrapment of the after-coming disproportionately large fetal head. At twenty-five weeks, for sure, cesarian section would have been indicated. C-section delivery is not indicated at twenty-three weeks. An operative delivery at that early time in gestation places the mother's health at considerable risk without any measurable benefit to the child. A less-experienced perinatologist might have given in to the parents' demands for cesarian section. Sam had been in the business for thirty years. He knew the ninety-five percent plus odds that the baby would not survive, no matter the mode of delivery.

By the time a half-awake Craig arrived in the delivery room, little Tracey was three minutes old. He found her blue and struggling to breathe. Although he personally didn't believe resuscitation was warranted, he placed an *endotracheal tube* in her airway in compliance with the family's wishes. By the current neonatal ethical guidelines he was duty-bound to allow competent parents to make the decision to pursue life as early as twenty-three weeks; some neonatologists might have said as early as twenty-two weeks.

Tracey was born in 1998. Ten years later, a website from the National Institutes of Health was developed, which allowed calculation of survival and quality of survival in infants less than twenty-five weeks based on five characteristics: birth weight, gestational age, sex, singleton versus multiple birth, and administration of antenatal steroids. According to this website Tracey's chance of survival without moderate or severe impairment would have been estimated at four percent.[3]

Craig, Marcia, the neonatal nurse, and Jerri, the respiratory therapist, hurriedly whisked the baby off down a short hallway to the NICU. On arrival in the NICU, Tracey was ice-cold; her rectal temperature registered only ninety degrees. Her precipitous delivery didn't permit the resuscitation team adequate time to preheat the warmer bed in the delivery room, nor to set up a warming mattress. Tracey's skin was tissue-paper thin, gelatinous-appearing. Already it was peeling off over her legs in the areas where the obstetrician had grabbed her in order to deliver her. She weighed just over one pound. Tracey's eyes were tightly fused, like a newly born puppy's. Thin gelatinous skin with early breakdown and fused eyes are reliable signs of extreme prematurity, confirming that the twenty-three weeks was an accurate assessment of gestational age. Despite maximal settings on the ventilator, the infant's oxygen saturation, the level of oxygen in her arterial blood, read only sixty-five percent, as opposed to a barely acceptable lower limit of eighty percent. Based on her extreme prematurity, low body temperature, and severe lung problems, her chances of survival were nearly zero.

Jerri gave a dose of *surfactant* down her endotracheal tube, and there was some slight improvement in the level of oxygen in her blood. Tracey's blood pressure was so low that it didn't register with a blood pressure cuff, and it was barely measurable from her arterial line even with a sophisti-cated electronic transducer. This problem was yet another ominous sign for Tracey. Standard therapeutic measures with fluid administration and potent cardiac drugs did not have much effect in raising her blood pres-sure. The staff thought that little Tracey wouldn't survive much beyond sunrise. The nurses, doctor, and respiratory therapists uniformly believed her death might be for the best. Should she survive the first night, she faced an incredible struggle for life, with ongoing suffering for months. Her prognosis for survival or normal development was poor no matter how aggressively they were to treat her current problems and future ail-ments as they arose.

The blood vessels lining the fluid spaces within the immature brains of extremely premature infants like Tracey are fragile. There's a tendency, especially if the infant is critically ill, for these vessels to rupture, resulting in brain hemorrhages of varying degrees of severity. These *intraventricular hemorrhages (IVH)* can be quite large and life threatening. And so was the case with Tracey. A cranial ultrasound on the second day of life revealed massive hemorrhages on both sides of her brain, not a surprising finding in light of her moribund condition at birth. Her ventricles, the fluid-filled small spaces within the brain substance, were already enlarged, swollen with blood. In addition, a large amount of blood was visible within the brain substance itself. These large clots compressed and destroyed potential brain cells and future synaptic connections that would have enabled Tracey to move her limbs, to think, and to reason. Little Tracey's chance of anything resembling normal development was as close to zero as it could be without being zero.

The High Price of Heroics

When a devastating event occurs, one that will most certainly effect either survival or a good neurological outcome, the treating physician should be frank with the family. When I find myself in that role, although I seek to be compassionate, I don't lie about the future. As surrogate decision makers for their minor children, parents have the right and responsibility to choose the therapies and support they deem best for their children. They have the same rights and responsibilities to decline the treatments that in their opinion offer little or no benefit. The law ensures that parents will be the final decision makers. It is the physician's job to make sure that the parents know the medical facts before they are asked to agree to a suggested treatment course, or before they make the decision to forego treatment. We hope that they are aware of all the facts before they go so far as to demand a specific treatment. The issue presents dual responsibilities: responsibility of the physician to explain and responsibility of the parent to make the wisest choice.

As the daytime doctor, I inherited Tracey's care. I met with the T's in our conference room to discuss the wisest course of action. As sympathetically as possible (and I really have to try hard with situations like this, ones that I deem futile), I talked with Mom and Dad about Tracey's near-hopeless chance for survival, and the bleak outlook for future mental and physical development. Words like severe mental retardation, *shunt* procedures, cerebral palsy, wheelchair bound, and life-long custodial care were bandied about. The discussion included much information, usually more than the average family can digest in one sitting. Families often need to hear the same information multiple times over several days, sometimes even over the course of several weeks before it sinks in. We neonatologists dread these conferences behind closed doors. Not only are we conveying very bad news, but we know we're leading up to a discussion of a possible Do Not Resuscitate order, limitation of aggressive therapy, or even withdrawal of life support. There will be tears, sometimes even hysterical crying and wailing, in the presence of which most of us medical professionals feel—and are—totally inadequate.

In Tracey's case, however, no tears were shed. The family appeared to be oblivious to the import of what I had just said. They were in complete denial. Denial is actually a stage of grief; they had no control over the battle between their emotions, their intellect, and reality. They wanted their baby to survive. They did not believe that desire was unrealistic.

"Doctor, we love our daughter. We want to take her home in a few months when she's ready. We think she will do better than you expect. But no matter how handicapped she is, we will love her just the same." Mr. T spoke for the couple. The T's honestly believed those last two statements to be true. I suspected that they doubted the veracity of what I was telling them about Tracey's current condition, and about my medical prediction of her poor prognosis. When a child is a baby, this self-deception is easy to slip into. Even normal newborns are helpless, so any baby that is helpless can appear normal. As the baby grows, the reality of the child's limitations compared to the neighbors' babies grows too, and becomes difficult to bear. At this early stage, Tracey's parents still believed that she'd be fine. Forty-eight hours previously they had anticipated a daughter born at term. They anticipated a child who would be the delight of her grandparents' retirement years. They anticipated a daughter who would grow up all too soon, go to college, have a career, perhaps even own a small but growing trucking business as her parents were doing. They may have had daydreams about an outdoor wedding: Tracey dressed in a beautiful white gown and veil, strolling down the aisle on her father's arm to the strains of Wagner's "Wedding March." Perhaps they even had visions of Tracey with adorable babies of her own. Now, a short forty-eight hours later, they couldn't fathom the loss of that vision. To face the end of their dream at this point in time would be much too sudden, much too painful.

Death is reality. When a baby dies, the dream dies. Rational people cannot deny death when it occurs. But the dying process and certain disability in the future can be denied for a long, long time. And modern technology allows, even encourages, this don't-think-about-it-now scenario. We plod on with treatment after painful and expensive treatment although we know our efforts are futile. The medical establishment doesn't say no so long as the patient or family says yes!

When Tracey's respiratory condition worsened the next day, Craig—back on call for the weekend—offered the T's the opportunity to either make Tracey's status "Do Not Resuscitate," or to withdraw ventilatory support and allow her to pass away quickly and painlessly in their comforting and loving arms. I could picture his flat affect, arms crossed across his chest, as he offered these alternatives in his deep resonant voice.

"No DNR, no withdrawal of support" was the parents' emphatic answer. "Let's give her a chance. We know she's going to be all right." Read between the lines: *We don't believe you. We don't trust you, or anyone else in this neonatal unit. You don't care about us. You don't care about our baby. Maybe you think our daughter isn't worth the trouble or expense. You don't know everything. You don't have a crystal ball.* These are not atypical thoughts for parents confronted with situations like Tracey's. One learns not to take it personally. One learns to keep the lines of communication open. One learns to keep one's curt response of frustration to oneself.

We continued applying our medications and advanced technology to Tracey's illnesses without limitations. Her immature lungs succumbed to the deleterious effects of lifesaving oxygen and ventilation. At four days of age she developed an air-leak syndrome, with *pulmonary interstitial emphysema (PIE)*. Air had dissected into the lung substance, and appeared on her chest X ray as circular and linear lucencies on her chest film, which we call *PIE* (pronounced P-I-E). PIE had stiffened her lungs further. Since the advent of surfactant, the incidence of PIE has declined markedly, but it still occurs occasionally in our smallest and sickest infants. Three days after the chest X ray had first shown PIE, her right lung ruptured, causing a massive *pneumothorax* (free air inside her chest). Tracey's heart rate fell precipitously. My colleague, Dr. Halsted, inserted an emergency chest tube and the acute crisis passed. Over the course of the ensuing week, various neonatologists inserted five more chest tubes into her little chest. Each procedure rescued her from certain death. Although Tracey was on frequent doses of painkillers, and we also used incision-site skin infiltration with a local anesthetic agent, chest tubes have got to be uncomfortable. Adults who are conscious when they suffer a tension pneumothorax report that the sensation of shortness of breath and pressure in the chest are terrifying. The severity of Tracey's lung problems was such that she'd remain ventilator-dependent for the first two months of her life.

When Tracey was one week old, my junior colleague, Dr. Phyllis Gray, noted a heart murmur, which we suspected was a *patent ductus arteriosus (PDA)*, a common complication of extreme prematurity.[4] Tracey's lungs were flooded with fluid on account of the PDA. Dr. Gray ordered an *echocardiogram* or ultrasound of the heart. The noninvasive bedside procedure revealed a large PDA. Dr. Gray then ordered a course of *intravenous* indomethacin, the same anti-inflammatory drug that you and I take in pill form for aches and pains. Indomethacin is a prostaglandin inhibitor. Inhibiting *prostaglandin* reduces inflammation and pain, which is why it works for headaches and the like. Prostaglandin is also the substance that keeps the *ductus* open. Inhibiting prostaglandin with indomethacin allows the ductus to close in seventy percent of infants. A repeat echocardiogram showed that Tracey's ductus had closed. The treatment apparently had worked. One week later, however, her ductus opened again, but this time medication didn't work. If her PDA were to have stayed open, Tracey's already damaged lungs would have continued to worsen. To rid her of the pesky PDA, she required surgery. The surgeon would have to make a generous incision on Tracey's left side and open her tiny chest. He'd then have to find the ductus, be sure that he didn't entrap any nerves, and then position a tiny steel clip on the offending blood vessel. Then sutures would be placed on either side of the clip, and the ductus would be severed. If we had decided not to ligate the offending blood vessel, Tracey's lungs would have continued to deteriorate, and she might have died within weeks of pulmonary failure or a massive pulmonary hemorrhage.

Mom and Dad consented to the invasive risky surgery to keep their daughter alive. Following PDA surgery, Tracey's condition stabilized, but she made little progress toward being weaned off the ventilator. In desperation we started Tracey on a course of steroids. In 1998 we used a lot of steroids. "Nobody should die without the benefit of steroids" is a bad joke left over from the 1970's. For many years we had recognized the complications of steroid treatment in the newborn: risk of infection, immune suppression, poor growth, gastrointestinal bleeding, high blood sugar, and high blood pressure. Brain damage—specifically the increased chance of developing cerebral palsy—had yet to be recognized as a possible outcome of neonatal steroid use. That complication would be recognized with the advent of the meta-analysis, a statistical technique that combines the results of many different studies on hundreds of patients, performed by different investigators in separate institutions, thereby increasing the power to find a small difference between two therapies.

At first Tracey's lung condition improved slowly in response to steroids. However, at two and half weeks of life, during her prolonged steroid course, her condition took a nose dive. Suddenly Tracey required increased oxygen and higher pressures on the ventilator in order to maintain her blood gases in a range compatible with life. Her blood sugar shot up to four times the normal value, forcing us to administer insulin as if she were a diabetic. High blood sugar under these circumstances is most likely due to bacterial infection. Dr. Penny Strauss, the neonatologist on call that night, surmising that Tracey was probably infected—"septic" in medical jargon—drew a blood culture and started our little patient on potent broad-spectrum antibiotics. Dr. Strauss wanted to do a spinal tap to see if Tracey also had meningitis, but Tracey did not tolerate being turned on her side and bent into a "C" curve, her back convex, and knees to chest for the procedure. Placed in this position, her heart rate dropped and she turned blue, so Dr. Strauss abandoned the attempt.

The next morning the lab called to tell me that the blood culture, drawn only ten hours previously, was already showing the presence of bacteria. Playing the odds, we had empirically started Tracey on what proved to be the appropriate antibiotic choice. After twenty-four hours of medication, Tracey was stable enough for the spinal tap. The fluid we obtained from her back looked like cloudy Coca-Cola, a combination of old blood and bacteria and white cells. Walt, a previous neonatal colleague of mine, long since departed for the west coast, used to describe the appearance of spinal fluid in terms of liquid refreshment. When a baby has a cerebral hemorrhage, the red blood cells break down and are eventually digested by white cells in the spinal fluid. Within a week of a brain hemorrhage the spinal fluid looks like Coca-Cola. Over the course of about two to three weeks, Walt would announce its progression to burgundy wine, bourbon, sweet tea (iced tea to Yankees), scotch, apple juice, and finally water, as the blood cell remnants were removed and the fluid cleared to its normal appearance. Tracey had *staphylococcus aureus* meningitis. The bacteria were eating away at her already damaged brain, adding infectious insult to injury from her previous massive hemorrhage.

Soon Tracey's head began to grow at an alarmingly rapid rate, much greater than the upper limit of normal, which is one and a half centimeters per week. The pressure in her brain was building up, probably because of the previous bleeding, although there may have been a contribution from meningitis as well. Adults with increased pressure in the brain (increased intracranial pressure in Med-speak) have horrid, severe headaches. Adults are at risk for death from compression of the brainstem, the area of the brain closest to the spinal canal, the area that controls respiration and blood pressure. Newborn skulls, on the other hand, are made up of eight separate bones. This gift of nature allows for growth of the brain as the baby matures. Increased intracranial pressure in newborns, therefore, results in rapid expansion of head size but not face size, and severe compression of the brainstem doesn't usually occur. Repeated serial head ultrasounds confirmed rapid fluid enlargement of Tracey's ventricles. What brain substance was left was compressed to a narrow rim inside the skull surrounding the huge fluid-filled ventricles. She now looked *hydrocephalic*—a giant head and sweet normal-sized face on a scrawny body. Tracey had almost doubled her birth weight (although much of this weight gain was fluid in her enlarged head), but she still weighed less than two and a half pounds. How were we to remove this excess fluid to prevent further compression of her brain tissue? And if we allowed her head to enlarge by leaps and bounds, allowed her to develop severe hydrocephalus, she'd become increasingly hard to care for as positioning became more difficult.

When I was an intern, I had cared for a five-year-old child who had been admitted for treatment of his previously untreated congenital hydrocephalus. He weighed only fifteen pounds. His head circumference was sixty centimeters, the size of a watermelon! As the attendants gently lifted him off the stretcher into a crib, I heard them say, "Okay, Joe, you take the head and I'll take Jimmy's body." The unfortunate child had been born in 1969 with congenital hydrocephalus. His parents were told that he'd die and that trying to treat the enlarged head was useless. Jimmie was placed in a home for "incurables." His care was so good that he didn't die. He had become impossible to care for because of the size of his head, so he had been brought in for a corrective procedure, a *ventriculoperitoneal shunt (VP)*. The procedure would drain and recirculate the fluid internally on a continuous basis, and allow his huge head to shrink to a more normal size. This usual treatment for hydrocephalus, VP shunt, was not an option for Tracey at that point in time. Not only was she too small for the procedure, but her cerebrospinal fluid was too thick and proteinaceous to flow through the pressure valve of the shunt.

In 1998, the year of Tracey's birth, neurosurgeons had not reached a consensus on the optimal therapy for infants like Tracey, for whom standard shunts could not be performed. The options included surgery to place a reservoir—a surgically implanted plastic bulb that sits under the skin of the scalp and pokes a tentacle-like tube into the swollen ventricle of the brain. The neurosurgeon could put a needle into the reservoir and draw out fluid as frequently as needed to relieve the pressure. On the other hand, without placing a reservoir, the neurosurgeon could insert a needle directly through the fontanel (soft spot), through the remaining brain, and into the ventricle and withdraw fluid directly, obviating the need for a surgical procedure. Each time the needle passed through brain substance, a tract could form and fill with fluid increasing the potential for more brain damage. Introduction of a foreign body—a needle—into the reservoir or the brain or the spinal canal always carries the risk of infection. An alternative is for the neonatologist to perform a spinal tap to remove fluid every day or every other day, but eventually repeated spinal taps cease to work.

Because of Tracey's small size and precarious lung status, the only choice was repeated ventricular taps. Tracey underwent those for two months. Each time fluid was withdrawn it was sent to the lab for analysis. We were especially interested in the protein content of the fluid. Tracey's protein level was more than four times normal because of the protein from the disintegrating red cells in the fluid. The abnormally high level didn't begin to come down for a long time, even though the red cells had cleared. The additional protein likely represented brain melt, perhaps due to damage from the previous bleed, perhaps from meningitis; the destroyed brain cells were dying and their content being absorbed into the fluid. Brain melt is a very poor prognostic sign. The T's did not want to hear about Tracey's brain damage—not from me, not from my neonatal colleagues, not from the nurse practitioner, not from the bedside nurse, not from the neurologist, not from the neurosurgeon. All would be fine. Just wait and see.

We were desperate to help Tracey's parents understand what had happened to their daughter's brain. I suggested to the team that we actually show her parents Tracey's CT scan, pointing out to them the fluid buildup and holes in her brain. We could obtain a normal CT scan to compare, like a neonatal show-and-tell. Although they were not health care professionals, surely seeing what we saw would enable them to visualize the loss of brain tissue. Perhaps then they might understand what its destruction would mean for their daughter. The team agreed. We scheduled a multidisciplinary conference with the family.

I'd done this sort of show-and-tell once before. Mr. W didn't believe his otherwise normal-appearing son Peter had developed *PVL (periventricular leukomalacia)*. PVL is a softening and destruction of the white brain matter that surrounds the lateral ventricles of the brain.[5] Its presence correlates well with future development of cerebral palsy. Peter had significant cystic areas that showed up as dark circles in the white-appearing normal brain tissue on cranial ultrasound. When Peter's dad, who had previously been in total denial about the problem, saw the head ultrasound, he remarked, "My God, you could drive a f---ing truck through there!" I took that comment to mean he understood that Peter would probably have developmental problems as he grew older. A picture, in this case, was certainly worth more than a thousand words.

The T's stared at the X ray view box on which I had hung their daughter's CT scan as well as a normal scan for comparison. Their expressions were blank. Despite the fact that they were both high school graduates and had a small independent trucking business, they appeared unable to grasp the significance of having a fluid-filled brain instead of a brain full of normal neurons. Mom turned to me, and asked innocently, "But the brain will grow back as she gets older, won't it?"

"No," I replied, "the amount of fluid may go down after Tracey has her shunt placed, but the brain matter that has been destroyed will not grow back." *Not ever, no matter how much you wish for it or pray for it,* I wanted to add, but held back. I was frustrated, bordering on angry. I hoped my voice didn't betray me. Fortunately, I had never been in a position where I was told bad news repeatedly and continued to deny it. I could not imagine having such a shield of denial in place. This discussion was at least the twentieth time they had heard the same story: brain damage that was severe and would not go away, a baby who would be multihandicapped if she survived, a child who was likely to need ongoing supervision in the activities of daily life, and a baby who would never outgrow her infancy. None of the health care team had figured a way to get the message through to this family. It was a source of great frustration to the medical and nursing staff. I suspected that our failure to communicate was also a source of frustration to the T's. *Why don't they leave us alone?* they must have thought. *Don't they know we don't want to hear about their awful predictions anymore?*

When Tracey was three weeks old, I had noted on her daily physical exam that a previously flat pink one-centimeter round spot on her right forearm was now raised. The tiny lesion blanched when pressed, the telltale sign of a capillary hemangioma.[6] Tracey's hemangioma began to enlarge rapidly when her steroid course ended. The steroids had evidently been keeping its growth in check. The hemangioma grew quite unsightly. Her mother told me that she knew it was the result of a bad intravenous line, because a nurse had told her that. I doubted that a nurse had said anything so outrageous and clinically incorrect. What could a nurse have said that could be misconstrued to mean what Tracey's mom had claimed? At this point in time Tracey's bedside nurse noted that Mrs. T kept a notebook in her purse. She made entries into it every day. Parents most certainly have a right to keep a journal. We even encourage the practice. When the child survives, it makes a meaningful keepsake, reminding the parent of the good and the bad of the neonate's NICU stay. If the baby doesn't make it, the journal is a testimony to the baby's fight for life. But the way Mrs. T surreptitiously made entries from time to time sent off vibes of future lawsuits.

Once I cared for a tiny patient whose mother was a Jehovah's Witness, and therefore was religiously bound not to accept blood products for herself or to allow blood transfusions even to save her baby's life. She had given birth to Amelia at twenty-four weeks gestation. Amelia weighed less than a pound and a half. She was anemic at birth, and had low *platelets* as well. Under normal circumstances we would have transfused Amelia with both platelets and blood. Her mother would not sign consent for either blood product. My partner, Dr. Cynthia James, decided that the baby would probably die that night anyway, so why aggravate Mom? Why make Mom worry that her baby would be, according to her beliefs, damned forever by receiving into her body someone else's blood? However, Amelia did not die that first night, and we quickly changed course and pursued the transfusion issue. Standard operating procedure is to petition for a court order to allow administration of blood and/or blood products to save life or limb. The infant's family is entitled to a hearing, although in the case of a neonate the judgment is always in favor of allowing transfusion under a narrow set of extreme circumstances. The courts recognize the medical value of blood transfusions. Our courts will not allow parents to force their religious will on the incompetent minor child if it will endanger his life or welfare. Nevertheless, most Jehovah's Witnesses insist that we go through with the hearing. The Witnesses' spokespersons meet with the physician, social worker, and judge, often right in the neonatal conference room rather than in a court room. The out-of-court session takes one to two hours. All the facts regarding the need for blood transfusion and the Witnesses' religious and scientific testimony to the contrary must be heard. The judge then makes the decision to allow blood products or not to allow them. The ruling is always in favor of the hospital that wants to save the baby's life with a transfusion. The transfusions, however, are always limited to lifesaving measures. In addition, they are time limited according to the discretion of the judge, sometimes for one month, sometimes only for that one transfusion. When time runs out, court-directed action must be sought again, although another hearing is not necessary.

Most Jehovah's Witnesses say no more about transfusions. They have had their day in court. Occasionally parents are relieved that their infant's life will be saved and that they did not have to abandon their faith to see that it happened. The court decision removes responsibility from them. Ameilia's mother, however, remained antagonistic about the transfusions she received. Several weeks into her hospital course, she was still campaigning against any further transfusion. I stood at the bedside and talked to her again, going over the same issues about the need for platelets or blood. I heard a click. Down in the corner of the bed was a tape recorder. She was recording our conversation! She denied that she was recording it; it was a tape she was playing for her baby. When I asked to hear it, she declined.

Tracey had other complications typical of extreme prematurity as well. She sustained severe but temporary liver damage from *hyperalimentation*. A fungal infection in her bloodstream seeded her kidneys and required four weeks of antifungal therapy to clear. The diuretics that she received for her lung problems led to kidney stones, which cleared without specific therapy. Tracey's eyes showed rapidly *progressive retinopathy of prematurity (ROP)*. Laser therapy to both eyes halted the process, but the extent of her eye disease placed her at great risk for retinal detachments in the future. In addition, her optic nerves did not develop properly because of increased pressure on them from her intracranial hemorrhage and hydrocephalus. The pediatric ophthalmologist warned the family that Tracey's prognosis for useful vision was guarded.

When bad things happen and parents have been forewarned, reporting to them about each complication as it occurs can be like saying, "I told you so." I felt guilty talking to the T's about each complication, as if I should have tried harder to make them understand how unfair their persistence of therapy was for Tracey. It was a tremendous effort for me (and I suspect for all my colleagues) not to sound self-righteous or arrogant under these circumstances. I had no desire to make the parents feel more guilt than they probably already did. The decision for life was, unfortunately, also a decision for continued suffering.

At sixteen weeks of age Tracey finally received her shunt, and she was discharged home about a week after her mother's due date. Her first readmission to the hospital was one month after discharge for a malfunctioning shunt that required more surgery. Over the next six months she was admitted five times for various ailments related to her shunt and lung infections. When last examined in developmental clinic, Tracey was blind. She had developed severe cerebral palsy involving all four limbs *(spastic quadriplegia)*. At the age of two years, her developmental level was that of a two-month old. Her mother was no longer driving a truck. Tracey, with her ongoing physical therapy and multiple doctors' appointments, comprised her mother's full-time job. Her husband was now Corporal Kurt T. The now-military family had qualified for the Exceptional Family Member program of the United States Armed Forces, meaning that they were promised assignments to areas close to major medical centers for the sake of the ongoing care of their multiply handicapped child.

There are myriad books written by angry and disappointed neonatal parents who say, "They never told me my baby might be handicapped." As I read them I marvel at the deafening powers of denial because I know that the information was presented to the parents. There are other books that claim, "They said he wouldn't survive, and he did" or "They said she'd be abnormal, but she is fine." We neonatologists don't have crystal balls. We go with statistics. And we can be wrong. Somebody makes up the ten percent of survival or normal outcome. But I've yet to read the parent-written book based on the premise: "They said it would be bad, and I didn't believe them. But it was true; it was all true. I know that now and would not have made the same decisions I made then."

1. Fetal Intensive Care Unit.
2. Placenta accreta is a rare condition in which the placenta grows into the wall of the uterus. After delivery it doesn't detach. The patient bleeds profusely and usually requires a hysterectomy to control the blood loss. It occurs much more commonly in a uterus that has undergone a previous operative delivery, especially a classic (up and down) incision on the uterus.
3. http://www.nichd.nih.gov/about/org/cdbpm/pp/prog_epbo/epbo_case.cfm
4. As a fetus, each of us has a small blood vessel that connects the main artery going to the body (the aorta) with the main artery going to the lungs (pulmonary artery). This extra blood vessel (the ductus arteriosus) acts as a conduit to direct blood away from the lungs in utero. After all, the placenta is the organ of respiration before birth and our lungs are essentially biding their time until we're required to breathe air. Teleologically, this phenomenon of stealing blood away from the lungs in utero makes sense. Why waste cardiac output on the superfluous lungs? The ductus normally constricts soon after birth in response to the increased oxygen level outside the uterus, effectively closing down this conduit. In preterm infants the ductus may not respond to oxygen, and can stay open indefinitely. But because the pressure in the lungs is now lower than before birth, the direction of blood flow changes: too much blood goes to the lung, worsening lung status.
5. PVL has a ninety-percent correlation with the future development of cerebral palsy. It's important to make the diagnosis of PVL as soon as possible, so that the child can begin to receive appropriate physical therapy to avoid contractures and to maximize potential. PVL appears as cysts, sometimes tiny, usually middle-sized, occasionally very large, on cranial ultrasound. The best time to diagnose PVL by ultrasound in a preterm infant is between thirty-four and thirty-six weeks gestation. MRI is used for confirmation and to evaluate the extent of the damage.

6. A capillary hemangioma is a collection of blood vessels just under the surface of the skin. The lesion usually starts off very small, sometimes even pinpoint in size. It may get bigger with time, so big in fact that it risks deforming the limb in which it is located. If located on the face, the growth may distort facial features. It may interfere with vision if it develops near the eye. Although laser treatment is available, most hemangiomas resolve on their own and do not require intervention. Following a period of rapid enlargement, they begin to autodestruct, usually from the center outward. Eventually they disappear, leaving only a small scar. Occasionally their growth becomes unchecked, almost like a cancer. Such aggressive hemangiomas may respond to steroids, or in desperate cases, interferon therapy. Laser therapy and the like are reserved for the largest ones, for ones that threaten life, limb, or vision, or for those that occur in cosmetically important areas.

9

A Tale of Two Trisomies: Stephan

An Awful Discovery

"Dr. Sacks, I need you to come over here for a minute. Take a look at Baby Boy C's hands. I guess I didn't notice this before." Terry, a veteran of fifteen years' service as a nurse in the NICU sounded very concerned, almost frightened. Why so much anxiety about an infant's hands? If Terry had been voicing concern over an *IV* infiltrate, no matter how bad, she would have said "hand," not the plural, "hands." Or she simply would have stated the obvious: "Come look at this bad IV infiltrate."

In retrospect, Terry's facial expression revealed her dismay at missing an obvious problem. I missed that clue. Interpreting body language wasn't (and still isn't) my forte.

Stephan C was now four weeks old. When he was born by emergency cesarian section nearly three months before his due date, he had weighed only 527 grams, a mere one pound two and a half ounces. That vital statistic placed his prenatal growth well below the tenth percentile. In other words, more than ninety out of one hundred babies delivered at the same point in pregnancy were larger than he was. His weight was so low that it was barely half that of the average weight of an infant born at the same stage of pregnancy at which he was born. To give a more familiar analogy, this severe degree of growth failure was akin to a baby carried to full term who weighed only three pounds.

There is a name for Stephan's condition; he suffered from *IUGR, intrauterine growth restriction.* For many years IUGR had stood for intrauterine growth retardation. As the world became more politically correct, the "R" word was changed. Although the growth referred to in the acronym IUGR typically refers to weight, infants with IUGR usually have stunted length as well. Head circumference may also be affected, but most often it is spared. When nutrients in utero are in short supply, the fetus sustains brain growth as long as it can at the expense of corporeal growth. In Stephan's case all three parameters were severely affected. Most babies with benign IUGR exhibit head sparing. Brain growth as reflected in head circumference is preserved or impaired to a lesser extent than weight. In such cases of head sparing, cerebral volume and nerve cell multiplication have been preserved at the expense of development of body fat, bone deposition, and muscle growth. That was not the case with Stephan. All his body measurements lay well below the tenth percentile.

Stephan's conception was unexpected but welcome. Mrs. C had undergone fertility treatments for years. Three times she had taken Clomid, the fertility drug that induces ovulation. Unfortunately the couple's three other attempts at baby making had all terminated in early spontaneous miscarriage, and the couple had been advised to discontinue the drug. Mrs. C had just celebrated her forty-third birthday. She was medically guilty of the offense of AMA—advanced maternal age. She, her husband, and her obstetrician were aware of the evermore loudly ticking of her biological clock. The C's desperately wanted a child. After careful soul searching they had decided that adoption was not an option for them. They wanted a genetic, biologic child. Given Mrs. C's age and reproductive track record, they thought Stephan to be their last chance for biological parenthood.

The early weeks of pregnancy had been an exciting time, especially as the eighth, tenth, and then twelfth week passed. Those milestones had marked the times at which the other three pregnancies had been lost. The joy of this current pregnancy, however, was short-lived. At the sixteen-week visit Mrs. C's obstetrician had noted that the fetus was much too small for sixteen weeks. The fetus had developed severe growth restriction. Mrs. C had been referred to a high risk obstetrician, a *perinatologist*, for further evaluation. The early onset and severe degree of fetal growth impairment set off an alarm for him. There was no evidence of maternal illness or hypertension that might have explained fetal growth difficulties. And he knew that Mrs. C was in an age range indicative of increased incidence of chromosomal abnormalities. She had previously been offered a blood test and genetic amniocentesis to check for extra or missing chromosomes, but had decided against any genetic testing.

At sixteen weeks the doctors had considerable anxiety regarding what might be causing the fetus' poor growth. None of the tests they had proposed, including reconsideration of amniocentesis to obtain chromosomes, had any therapeutic implications for the fetus, unless one considered abortion for a defective product of conception therapeutic for the fetus, a concept to which the C's along with many other Americans, Roman Catholic and otherwise, did not subscribe. Nothing could be done to treat or alleviate whatever abnormalities might have been found. Furthermore, testing might reveal a serious, even lethal abnormality with the C's baby. Mrs. C refused any more definitive testing. Declining (we never document *refusal*; that's got negative connotations; *declined* is neutral) further testing is a common response, especially among older more desperate expectant mothers. Their thoughts might be, *If I don't have the study done, then the bad outcome won't happen.*

During my pediatric residency, Dr. Dara McMillan, one of my junior physician colleagues and a devout Catholic, gave birth to her third child. Oliver had Down syndrome, or *Trisomy 21*. Dara was only twenty-nine years old at the time of Oliver's birth, and therefore, not in a high-risk group for bearing a child with Down syndrome. Giving birth to one infant with Trisomy 21, however, slightly increases the risk for another birth with Trisomy 21 in each subsequent pregnancy. Infants with Down syndrome frequently have physical problems such as congenital heart disease or intestinal blockages in addition to mild to moderate mental retardation. Oliver had no structural abnormalities, but he did have an intestinal problem that resulted in his needing a *colostomy* before he was a week old. With her next pregnancy Dara elected to have a genetic amniocentesis. I questioned her, asking, "If abortion is not an acceptable alternative for you, why have the test?"

"I want to be prepared," was her response. "If this next baby also has Down syndrome, I'll love her anyway, but I need to be prepared emotionally. I wasn't prepared for Oliver's problems, and that made it tougher to deal with them."

The C's felt no such need to be prepared. All would be well. It just had to be. This could be their last chance for a biological child.

At the time of Stephan's delivery by emergency cesarian section, he had been very sick. My neonatal colleagues in the operating room tried to revive him with routine bag-and-mask ventilation. But he was so little that even the smallest mask hadn't formed an effective seal over his mouth and nose. The doctors had been forced to *intubate* Stephan— to put a tube down his throat to breathe for him—if he was to have a chance to survive. Even though his weight was borderline for survival, his gestational age was fairly advanced. Survival rate at twenty-seven to twenty-eight weeks gestation overall was eighty percent in 1990, the year of Stephan's birth. After admission to the neonatal intensive care unit, the tiny baby had received surfactant for immature lungs and had then been stabilized on a ventilator.

It became obvious in retrospect that no health care professional had looked carefully and critically at Stephan's facial features or extremities during those first crucial hours. The admitting physician had noted that Stephan's ears were low-set—that is, the top of his pinna was located beneath an imaginary line drawn parallel and lateral from the outer corner of his eye. Low-set ears are a minor abnormality and in and of themselves do not cause alarm. But we hadn't noticed any of his other abnormalities, because we had tunnel vision.

For instance, a radiologist looks at an X ray because the internist suspects infection in the lungs. He finds the right middle lobe pneumonia, but misses the small metastatic breast cancer nodule in the fourth rib because he wasn't specifically looking for it. When a baby is admitted to the NICU, we are initially concerned with immediate life-threatening conditions: How are her lungs functioning? Is she oxygenating well? Is her blood pressure adequate? Is her circulation okay, or does she need a transfusion? Does she have an infection we need to address aggressively? Is there a heart murmur? During the crisis of stabilization, minor issues fall victim to benign neglect or tunnel vision. Or perhaps the unit was busy the night of Stephan's birth with too many admissions or too many really sick infants. Maybe the admitting neonatologist was overwhelmed with the work load, or harried or somewhat sleepy in the middle of the night. What was our excuse for not doing a more thorough examination?

With the *endotracheal tube* taped in place, the abnormal pixie-like qualities of Stephan's facial features had been obscured. Initially he had an arterial line securely taped down in his right hand, and an intravenous line in his left hand. From time to time during the first month of his life, Stephan had an IV line started in a foot as well. So it had been hard to examine his hands and feet systematically and carefully. I'm rationalizing, of course. We should have noted the other soft-sign abnormalities.

During the three and a half weeks that had passed since Stephan's inauspicious start, the health care team had put forth a maximal effort to preserve his life. Despite four doses of surfactant for his immature lungs, the severity of Stephan's RDS required very high pressures and rates on the ventilator. On the third day of life, blood poured out of his lungs, bubbling up the endotracheal tube. Despite constant suctioning of the blood we could no longer adequately oxygenate him. Without immediate improvement there was a good chance that the tiny baby would die. The respiratory therapists wheeled out our high-tech, *high frequency oscillator (HFOV)*, a newer distant cousin to the *high frequency jet ventilator (HFJV)*. With the aid of the oscillator, we could achieve rates of 480 to 900 breaths per minute. Rather than softly rising and falling with each ventilator breath, on the HFOV the infant's chest wiggles. Actually the infant wiggles from the neck to the navel. Although research studies do not show any difference in mortality rate in tiny babies treated with the HFOV rather than the conventional ventilator, our group strongly believed that the HFOV had the capacity to rescue these infants from respiratory failure and/or death. We claim to practice *evidence-based medicine*. But in this case we preferred our anecdotal experience to the metastudies in the medical literature. We wouldn't deny the patient the questionable benefits of the oscillator. It couldn't hurt now, could it?

An *echocardiogram* performed that same day confirmed that Stephan had a large *patent ductus arteriosus* (*PDA*), par for the course in such a tiny infant. Because of persistence of the open ductus, too much blood had circulated to his lungs causing rupture of capillaries and bloody pulmonary edema. The PDA was responsible for his lung hemorrhage. Fortunately he responded to standard medical treatment, which induced PDA closure.

We actually weren't looking for congenital heart disease, but the echocardiogram also revealed a large *ventricular septal defect (VSD)*, a hole in the thick muscular wall that separates the right ventricle from the left ventricle of the heart. Sooner or later this type of congenital heart disease would result in too much blood flow to Stephan's lungs. This overabundance of circulation typically throws infants into congestive heart failure. The heart failure can be controlled initially with digitalis and diuretics, but most children with a large VSD require open heart surgery before the age of one year.

Routine cranial ultrasound, done to ascertain whether Stephan had sustained any bleeding in his brain, a typical complication of very sick, very tiny preterm infants, showed a grade III (out of IV) hemorrhage. Blood filled the ventricles of his brain, and the ventricles were somewhat swollen. A grade III hemorrhage frequently leads to hydrocephalus and significant brain damage. The baby often shows evidence of severe neurological and/or developmental problems as he matures through childhood.

Stephan's lung disease progressed inexorably. It was so bad that we doctors decided to treat him with a potent steroid for ten days. The steroid course was calculated to decrease lung inflammation and allow weaning off the ventilator. About forty-eight hours after beginning the drug, Stephan's lung status began to improve slowly. The steroids continued to work their gradual magic, but in the end induced only modest improvement. Stephan's lungs were still not strong enough to support removal of the breathing tube and ventilator. Tiny Stephan remained dependent on oxygen and tethered to his ventilator.

On the eve of our awful discovery, Stephan, at nearly a month of age, already had four strikes against him, making survival and normal growth and development improbable. Strike one was early onset non-head sparing intrauterine growth restriction, a brain with far fewer cells than normal. Strike two was severe lung disease virtually unresponsive to steroids. Strike three was a large hole in his heart. Strike four was a substantial hemorrhage in his developing brain. But NICU activity isn't a game where we keep score. Strikes don't count in the NICU. We grant unlimited swings and misses to our players. The only umpires that can call a player out are parents making decisions in the best interests of their children and/or the failure of medical technology (otherwise known as death). Despite all of Stephan's horrific current and potential problems and the unlikelihood of survival, let alone intact survival, the C's continued to dream of a full recovery for their only child. They insisted that he would be just fine. They were vocally adamant that all measures be taken to support Stephan. And we doctors and nurses obediently complied with their wishes. Although his prognosis was extremely guarded, it was not impossible that he would survive. That was, however, until our discovery.

At this point, the staff already feared confrontation with the C's regarding the awful truth of Stephan's medical condition and poor prognosis based on medical facts and statistics. Bedside nurses who had spoken up about his current precarious condition and guarded future were reported by the family to nursing management, and found that they were not reassigned to care for Stephan. The list of nurses permitted to minister to Stephan grew shorter. The doctors' opinions were courteously ignored. Communication attempts were strained, and overall transfer of medical information from physicians to Stephan's parents was poor and restricted to only the current status details. Terry's startling discovery of Stephan's hands would abruptly end the denial, the dreaming, and the hopes. Or so I believed. Cloaked in DNA, organized into forty-seven legions, reality would at last declare its presence. Following its grand entrance, reality would settle in, and reign supreme. The finale, the end to Stephan's struggle, was approaching.

While removing the IV, which had dislodged from the vein and which we could no longer safely use, Terri noticed peculiar positioning of Stephan's tiny hand. When allowed its freedom, the appendage assumed a tightly clenched position with the index finger overlapping the third finger and the pinkie overlapping the ring finger. When Terri looked closely at the other hand, she noted the same phenomenon. Try to make your own fingers perform this maneuver. Maybe you can passively force them into position that way briefly, but they rapidly revert to normal configuration.

The sight of the hand sent shivers up my spine. How in Heaven's name had I missed this? And my colleagues, how had they missed it as well? Stephan was nearly a month old! Countless nurses had cared for him; all six neonatologists had examined him at one time or another, yet not one health care professional had made note of this most significant finding. The deformed hands were classic for *Trisomy 18*, also known as *Edwards syndrome*.

Denial

The cells of the affected Trisomy 18 infant contain three copies of the number eighteen chromosome instead of the normal complement of two. The syndrome is rare in live-born infants—only one in five-thousand births—and is much more common in children born to women over the age of thirty-five. Trisomy 18 presents as a constellation of cosmetic and structural defects, including this peculiar hand position. Afflicted children are slightly dysmorphic—unusual looking—at birth. The newborn with Edwards syndrome has a pixie-like face, low-set ears, prominent occiput or back of the head, and short broad chest with nipples spaced too far apart. Stephan had all four features. Children with Edwards syndrome frequently have feet deformities and always have the peculiar fisted appearance to their hands. Many babies have serious congenital heart defects (as did Stephan) or gastrointestinal malformations. Neurologically these children are profoundly impaired and rarely progress in development beyond the two- or three-month level.

Trisomy 18 is considered a uniformly lethal syndrome. Most Trisomy 18 conceptuses end in spontaneous abortions. Half of live-born Trisomy 18 infants die in the first week of life. Children with Trisomy 18 are described as feeble and are prone to central *apnea*.[1] There seems to be a disconnect in the child's respiratory control system and he simply forgets to breathe. The prognosis is so grim that the American Academy of Pediatrics recommends that if the diagnosis is certain that pediatricians undertake no heroic efforts to resuscitate these infants at birth.[2] Pediatric textbooks recommend comfort care only. In our infinite neonatal wisdom, we had seen to it that Stephan, known to us simply as a tiny growth-restricted preterm infant with multiple complex problems, survived his first month of life. He was entirely dependent on technological support, and most certainly the worse for wear.

I immediately drew blood for chromosomes. Our laboratory didn't process chromosome tests on site, so we sent off the specimen to our contracted reference laboratory for a definite diagnosis. Given Stephan's outward appearance and the presence of serious congenital heart disease, I was pretty certain that Stephan suffered from Trisomy 18. Since it would take one to two weeks to get the final results of the chromosome analysis, the following morning I had the dreaded family meeting in the conference room. I planned to introduce the diagnosis of Trisomy 18 and its terrible implications for the future. Simply, there would be no future for Stephan.

The meeting with the C's didn't go well. They refused to believe me, clinging to denial; it was their security blanket. Experts say that denial allows us to process only as much information as is bearable.[3] Without denial we would succumb to desolation. Over the course of the ensuing week, while we waited for the test results to come back, my partners and I counseled the C's daily as to what Trisomy 18 means. We beat them over the head with the information—that's really what it amounted to, a verbal beating. In their denial they demanded another chromosomal analysis, this time from a lab in Texas. We complied. It was easier than fighting. The results were the same: Stephan had Trisomy 18. No doubt about it. Chromosomes don't lie, especially when the expensive test had been repeated twice.

The C's then turned to the Internet seeking further information that might possibly contradict what the doctors were telling them. They finally accepted the lab-test confirmed diagnosis of Trisomy 18, but remained in denial of its implications.

The Internet has had a profound impact on the practice of medicine. Doctors can confirm almost any medical fact or look up a specific treatment without a trip to the medical library. Unfamiliar medication? Just Google it or check it out on Wikipedia or on the manufacturer's website. Case reports travel from continent to continent in real time. Reports of untoward side effects of drugs and treatments appear with lightning speed. Specialty listservs allow doctors to communicate with others in their own subspecialties daily. One can even query recognized experts and superdoctors whom one does not know personally. Via the Internet my hospital librarian can obtain ninety-seven percent of all my reprint requests electronically within twenty-four hours.

Conversely, patients can find out as much information about their own diagnoses as they wish. They can identify centers of excellence for their particular maladies. Computer-savvy patients frequently show up for office visits armed with printouts of information on the most recent treatments or alternative therapies. On the Internet one can locate support groups for the gamut of maladies: everything from major common ailments such as breast cancer, heart disease, and diabetes to the rarities of maple syrup urine disease, reflex muscular dystrophy, and Trisomy 18.

Several years ago I admitted a patient born with a massive cystic hygroma, a benign tumor of the lymphatic glands of the face and neck. The tumor had grown wildly in utero, and now extended from the infant's cheek area down through his upper chest. It was so large that it compressed his windpipe. In the delivery room he required placement of an endotracheal tube in his trachea to keep his airway open so he could breathe. When the child had initially been diagnosed prenatally with this particular tumor, his father, an engineer, had done a literature search. Dad found an alternative treatment to extensive surgery. The treatment, initially reported out of a hospital in Japan, involved injection of a bacterial toxin into the hygroma to sclerose or scar it down. When the infant, accompanied by his father's Internet printouts, was admitted to our NICU, a five-minute search on the Internet revealed a center in the midwestern United States that was conducting trials on utilization of this toxin. Following a few phone calls to the principal investigator and the baby's insurance carrier, our transport team took the baby by fixed wing (that's an airplane, as opposed to a helicopter in transport talk) to the Iowa center. The baby had a decent outcome.

Support groups for childhood diseases, many of which are genetic and cause severe handicaps, serve valuable functions. Even those groups which exist only in virtual reality on the Internet are useful. They ensure that families of affected children do not feel totally isolated. Families are reassured that their initial emotional responses of desperation, denial, and hopelessness are normal. The natural history of the disease is explained in terms parents can understand. The best Internet sites deal compassionately with the realities of family life with a profoundly handicapped child, one with ongoing onerous medical treatment and home management, or one with a limited life span. Concrete and practical suggestions for dealing with the problems of the activities of daily life of such children abound. Parents share anecdotes through their personal blogs. The overall influence of the Internet is definitely positive.

On the other hand, some web sites emphasize the extraordinary blessings of raising a severely multiply handicapped child. These sites give short shrift to the incredible challenges and downsides of rearing such a child, stressing instead the need for putting up the good fight against the pessimistic and uncaring medical establishment. They might emphasize the moral obligations of the parent to fight for every support, medication, or surgery the child needs, even if they cannot cure the child or even make the child's life more comfortable. Such sites point out how insurance companies and the federal government take delight in denying needed care. They draw lines in the virtual sand. Doctors, hospitals, and insurance carriers are on the wrong side of the line; we are the enemies in this battle.

"They said Marguerita would never show any progress, and now she can roll over!" So exclaims Marguerita's blog. Marguerita, afflicted with Trisomy 18, has at last mastered this skill at five years of age! Obviously the doctors were wrong, according to this blog. The blog, however, doesn't tell of the downside of the struggle against the inevitable. It ignores the emotional cost to the family. The blog disregards the psychological burden on siblings. Such sites show only the positive side of sharing in the care of the handicapped child. They emphasize the achievement of developmental milestones of the child with Trisomy 18, however small or severely delayed. They always describe the quality of the child's life as positive.

The C's located several websites regarding children with Trisomy 18. Many of these websites pointed out the wonderful experience parents have had caring for their babies during their tragically short lives. Stephan's parents emotionally attached themselves to a physician in a western state who had written extensively about lifesaving surgery in children with Trisomy 13 and 18. They claimed the hospital where he held surgical privileges would operate on Stephan's heart defect if he could gain enough weight to undergo risky open heart surgery.

Ten days after we first suspected the diagnosis of Trisomy 18, and three days after we confirmed it the second time, I again talked at length with the C's. Gently but firmly I told them for the umpteenth time about the bleakness of the situation regarding long-term survival and meaningful neurological development. Even knowing that they would probably refuse, I nevertheless suggested instituting a Do Not Resuscitate order (DNR). I went even further and asked that they seriously consider withdrawal of all heroic support that was now keeping Stephan alive and permit their son the comfort and dignity of dying a natural death in their arms. The poking and prodding and handling (I wanted to say *torture*, but I didn't) of neonatal intensive care treatment was pointless. It would not change his prognosis or provide comfort. Quite the contrary, given his size, his lung problems, and his heart disease in addition to his underlying chromosomal abnormality, treatment would only prolong his suffering and drag out the dying process.

"I'm concerned that we are no longer doing things *for* Stephan, we are just doing things *to* him. Treatment is not benefiting him," I told Stephan's parents. *That means it is time to stop treatment,* I thought to myself.

To my surprise, after overnight consideration on the subject, the C's agreed to a limited DNR—no cardiac medications. But they were insistent that Stephan remain on the ventilator as long as he needed it, even to the point of discharging him home on a ventilator. We would not withhold medications Stephan might require for treatment of infection, lung disease, heart failure, or other ailments. Only *adrenalin* to jump start his heart was off-limits.

A few weeks after we established the limited DNR status, Stephan's parents were visiting at the bedside when the tracheal tube through which he was being ventilated plugged off, immediately obstructing his airway. Stephan turned deep blue. Suctioning didn't relieve the problem and Stephan's heart rate plummeted to fifty. The C's watched as we performed cardiac massage and as Kate, the respiratory therapist, pulled out the endotracheal tube to relieve the obstruction. They stood by observing the procedure to insert a new tube. Kate performed bag-and-mask ventilation until Stephan was pink. Kate forced Stephan's mouth open manually and placed the cold metal laryngoscope blade over his tiny tongue. Then she pushed it forward and visualized his vocal cords. She attempted to insert a tube through the cords into the baby's windpipe, but the first attempt was unsuccessful. Stephan turned blue again. The second attempt succeeded. Since Stephan had no intravenous line in place, we could not give him any sedation or pain medication for the procedure. The trauma of this scenario on Stephan was lost on his parents. They did not perceive it as painful or traumatic for Stephan. The C's saw only that their son improved in color after the final maneuver was successful. He was still alive. That last fact was all that counted. Their baby was alive, which meant they were still parents. Someday soon they would take him home.

Continued Suffering

During the ensuing month we tried to wean Stephan off the ventilator. All attempts failed. We held another formal parent conference. Given Stephan's deteriorating condition and likelihood of death before discharge, I asked the family, once again, to consider removing ventilator support to allow a natural death. I felt at best like a broken record, at worst like I was badgering the family. Mom and Dad C replied to my request for discontinuing support that Stephan was "fighting for his life." They cited the statistics of prolonged survival to age three or five of the occasional child with Trisomy 18. Obviously they had gleaned this encouraging information from the various websites they had visited.

A parent conference is first and foremost a teaching session in which the doctor tries to help the family understand the problems their child is facing, and the family conveys to the doctor their level of understanding, their emotional state, and their wishes regarding their child's future care. I like to teach parents with analogies. I tried to explain to the C's that dealing with the deadliness of Trisomy 18 is not like fighting cancer. Even with end-stage cancer, continued treatment may prolong good quality survival for another few months during which time another newer, more powerful drug may become available. Each new drug represents another chance to beat the cancer or at least to prolong life of some degree of quality. Drugs, physical therapy, megavitamins, dogged perseverance will not beat the diagnosis of Trisomy 18. The C's, however, couldn't give up on their child. They wouldn't and couldn't let go. And so the doctors and nurses were not allowed to let go either.

Stephan continued to live in our NICU, ventilator-dependent for the next two months. On account of his extreme prematurity and long-time exposure to high levels of oxygen, his retinas developed abnormally. Our pediatric ophthalmologist had been following his eye exam carefully every other week since he was four weeks old. Now he had developed clear signs of stage 3 retinopathy of prematurity. The blood vessels on his retina were growing wildly. Unchecked, they would continue to grow, distorting his retina, possibly leading to retinal detachment. Without surgery he might go blind; with surgery he might still have severe visual impairment, and would most certainly lose some peripheral vision. When Stephan was three months of age, Dr. Varedo performed bilateral laser surgery on Stephan's retinas to try to preserve his vision. His overall condition was unstable following the stress of the operative procedure.

Stephan was afflicted with recurrent BPD spells. BPD stands for *bronchopulmonary dysplasia,*[4] a fancy name for the chronic lung disease that follows long-time ventilation and oxygen exposure in premature infants. During these BPD spells Stephan arched his back, acted air-hungry, gasped, turned deep purple then very pale, and dropped his heart rate to dangerously low levels. When we placed a stethoscope on his chest, air entry into his lungs was decreased or absent even though the ventilator continued to cycle.

Each spell eventually ended. Sometimes he responded to extra aerosol treatments, sometimes to subcutaneous injection of bronchodilating drugs, sometimes to increased pressures on the ventilator, sometimes to sedation, ultimately to tincture of time. I cannot imagine what the spells felt like to little Stephan. Certainly there was no cognitive aspect, as there would be with an adult: a feeling of suffocation, breathlessness, impending doom. But was it painful for him? When we hyperinflated his lungs, did his chest hurt? Did a rapid heart rate in response to bronchodilator medication produce cardiac pain? Was he exhausted when the spell finally broke?

We—the nurses, doctors, and respiratory therapists of the NICU—are the proximate cause of true suffering in our young, vulnerable patients. We poke and prod and insert needles and catheters and tubes. Many of these procedures are painful. We try to provide some type of pain relief, even if only minimally palliative, but many times the pain relief is only partial. But we always keep the end in sight—discharge home with Mom and Dad, and with luck and God's grace, a long, healthy, joy-filled, productive life. But for children with Trisomy 18 there can be no happy ending. How could we view the pain we inflicted on him as other than gratuitous, without higher purpose? Was satisfying unrealistic parental expectations a higher purpose? For me and the neonatal staff, Stephan's parents' continued insistence on heroic support was selfish, serving their own interests, not their child's. I was having increasing difficulty controlling my emotions, body language, and attitude when I dealt with the C's, and so were my physician, nursing, respiratory therapist, and social worker colleagues. Acting sympathetic and civil in situations like this is one of the biggest challenges of neonatal medicine.

When Stephan was three months old, we repeated an echocardio-gram to assess the status of his ventricular septal defect. Was it contribut-ing to his failure to wean off the ventilator? Was it time to start diuretic drugs or digitalis? The echocardiogram revealed that he had developed a significant degree of stenosis, or narrowing, of the pulmonary valve of his heart. This discovery changed his diagnosis from simple ventricular septal defect to *tetrology of Fallot*, a common form of serious cyanotic con-genital heart disease. The good news was that this obstruction at the pul-monary valvular level blocked too much blood from going to his lungs, thus preventing congestive heart failure from the large hole in his heart. The bad news was that this obstruction caused back-up of blood in the right ventricle of his heart. Within his heart, blue (unoxygenated) blood from the right side mixed with red (oxygenated) blood from the left side and then was pumped out into the general circulation. The mixture of unoxygenated and oxygenated blood lowered the overall level of oxygen in his arterial circulation. We agreed with the cardiologist's suggestion to lower the oxygen level we expected to achieve for Stephan. This plan meant we would need to give less oxygen to Stephan, which was good.

Multiple attempts to extubate Stephan, to get him off the ventila-tor—many of them resulting from his own struggling and dislodging his tube by his own efforts—were unsuccessful. The longest he lasted off the ventilator was thirty hours. We started him on oral prednisone, but this steroid treatment induced only minimal improvement. Just before Easter, when Stephan was already one month past his due date, the topic of *tracheostomy* and placement of a permanent feeding tube was intro-duced. The C's were undecided. They still harbored the irrational hope for a child who would soon breathe on his own and would take nourish-ment like other children by sucking from a bottle. It wasn't until three weeks later, in mid-May, that the family conceded that surgery for his airway and digestive tract was the only way that Stephan would be able to leave the hospital. The one goal which we all enthusiastically shared, staff and parents alike, was to get Stephan well enough to leave the hospi-tal. Although his future would be bleak, because his parents insisted, we were working to get him home with his parents, whatever that scenario might take. And it would take considerable equipment, personnel, parental training, and financial resources to accomplish our mutual, perhaps even futile, goal.

Five weeks after tracheostomy surgery to place a permanent breathing tube in his windpipe and *gastrostomy* to place a feeding tube in his stomach, at the age of six months, three months after what should have been his date of birth at term, Stephan was finally discharged home. He was off the ventilator, but still required oxygen administered by trach collar. Stephan's hospital bill was over $700,000, but the hospital would receive less than twenty percent of the billed charges from government-sponsored insurance. The neonatal case manager had arranged for Stephan to have around-the-clock skilled nursing care at home. The nursing care would be gradually weaned over the course of three months as his parents mastered the sophisticated skills necessary to care for their medically fragile child. A Medicaid program formerly known as the Katie Becket Waiver paid for the nursing care. This entitlement program enables families to care for children at home who otherwise would have to remain in the hospital separated from their loving families and at even greater expense to the taxpayer.

Stephan was readmitted to the hospital exactly one month after discharge for a three-day stay. His final admission to hospital was at the age of nine months. After two weeks of maximal critical care in the pediatric intensive care unit, Stephan finally died.

Total time at home with his family was sixty-two days, less than one quarter of his short life. I hope Stephan's struggles and suffering helped his family in some way because I do not believe prolonging his dying was of any benefit to Stephan himself.

1. K. L. Jones, ed., *Smith's Recognizable Patterns of Human Malformation*, 5th ed. (Philadelphia: W. B. Saunders Co., 1997).
2. John Kattwinkel M.D., ed., *Neonatal Resuscitation Textbook*, 5th ed. (American Academy of Pediatrics and American Heart Association, 2006).
3. Elisabeth Kübler Ross and David Kessler, *On Grief and Grieving* (New York: Scribner, 2007), p. 10.

4. Technically the term BPD is reserved for the lung disease that develops in infants who are born before thirty-two weeks gestation and are still in oxygen at thirty-six weeks post conceptual age, or one month before their due date (W. H. Northway, R. C. Rosan, and D. Y. Porter, "Pulmonary Disease Following Respirator Therapy of Hyaline-membrane Disease: Bronchopulmonary Dysplasia," *New England Journal of Medicine* 276, no. 7 [1967]: 357–68).

10

A Tale of Two Trisomies: Taylor Marie

Preparing For the Worst

In 1983, when I first started as a neonatologist in the medium-sized Southern city that I now call home, Bill F. was a senior registered respiratory therapist (RRT) in the NICU. He also was lead respiratory therapist on our neonatal transport team. Back then he looked as if he'd just stepped out of DaVinci's *Last Supper,* with long, straight, dark brown, shoulder-length hair dramatically parted in the middle; a full but trimmed beard; and deep-set dark serious eyes.

An apocryphal story concerning Bill made the rounds with all new members of the neonatal department. It seemed that one rainy summer night the neonatal transport team had been dispatched to a small community hospital in rural Georgia to pick up a seriously ill preterm infant. The infant's pediatrician had accurately counseled the mother that her little baby was in danger of dying from his severe lung problem. Needless to say, Mom was quite distressed, as are most mothers whose infants are snatched out of their arms (or out of their uterus, since some mothers don't get to hold their sick infants at all) and sent away to distant NICUs for desperately needed lifesaving treatment. Our team's exit procedure was to wheel the baby in the transport isolette into the mother's room on their way out to the waiting ambulance. If the mother had undergone a cesarian section under general anesthesia this opportunity might be the first time the mom would see her newly born child. Regrettably, for some mothers it might be the last opportunity they would have to bond with their critically ill babies before death would separate them forever.

The mom's swollen tear-stained face suddenly brightened as the team rolled into her room. "Thank you, Lordy! Thank you, Lordy! I knows Henry will be jus' fine. Jesus hisself be here to pick him up!" Mom was referring to Bill, attired in jeans, hospital-logo golf shirt, and sandals, and with his long hair, beard, and gaunt features, looking like an artistic rendering of a modern-day Jesus.

By 2006 Bill had long since left clinical respiratory therapy. For several years he worked in the research and development department of a medical device company. During that time he'd arranged for our hospital to participate in the clinical trials of a new piece of equipment (an early prototype of what is now an industry standard) for the noninvasive measurement of jaundice in newborns. During Bill's third professional career, he was a representative for a durable medical equipment company. During the seven years he worked in this capacity, I saw him occasionally when he came to our unit to educate a mother taking home her infant on an *apnea* monitor. In his fourth and current career he ran a sleep lab for a local pulmonologist.

In 2006 Bill's twenty-four-year-old daughter Grace H became pregnant with her first child. All had gone well until the most recent OB appointment. Grace's obstetrician had noted that the fetus' growth had slowed down, and referred Grace to a perinatologist for further testing. A level II ultrasound had revealed the fetus to have a major complex congenital heart defect: a double outlet right ventricle (DORV). Congenital heart disease is more common than one might imagine. It occurs in one to two percent of babies. But DORV is a rare entity, occurring in only one in 10,000 births.[1] Unfortunately it is often associated with major chromosomal abnormalities.

Bill called me and related the problems, asking for advice.

"Have they done chromosomes yet, Bill?" I asked hesitantly, hoping I wasn't suggesting a course of action that had not been proposed already.

He continued, "Grace will be seeing the perinatologist this week. She's going to have an amniocentesis to look for chromosomal problems. She's already thirty-three weeks pregnant now, so it's too late for a therapeutic abortion, even if she and my son-in-law wanted to go that route, which they don't and wouldn't have even if it were earlier in the pregnancy. But Grace and Buddy want to be prepared for the worst."

"It will be a good ten days to two weeks until you get the results," I replied. That's an eternity to wait to find out if your baby will be normal or not. "Bill, if you want me to, I'll be happy to talk with Grace and her husband when the results come back. If the chromosomes are okay, we can talk specifically about the heart defect. If the chromosomes are not okay, we can deal with that discussion too. You know that there will be important decisions to be made."

"Thanks. I'll let you know if they'll want to talk about it. I expect they'll want more information. I feel so awful for them. They want this baby so much. The nursery is ready for the baby. It's so beautiful with its enchanted garden theme." A long pause, then, "I appreciate your help, Dr. Sacks." We said our good-byes and hung up.

Since Bill was very specific that the doctors hadn't seen any other abnormalities, specifically no limb deformities, no finger abnormalities, no cleft lip, no small head or hydrocephalus, I was hopeful, as were Bill and his family, that the cardiac defect would be just an isolated, albeit serious, abnormality.

Two weeks later I arrived home after a long day dealing with very sick infants and their distraught parents, a ninety-minute nonproductive administrative meeting, and a computer malfunction that interfered with completing rounds. My husband told me there was a message from "somebody named Bill" on the answering machine, requesting me to call him back. Steve had deleted the message already, but handed me the phone number. Since I hadn't heard the message personally, my opportunity to judge the tone of voice, the presence of elation, or desperation was gone. I was clueless as to the chromosomal findings. Good? Bad? Actually

I guess they could still be unknown. If the cell culture had failed to grow, no chromosomes would have been harvested, and no immediate answer would have been provided for the H family. I dialed Bill's number immediately and he answered on the first ring.

"Dr. Sacks, it's not good news. My granddaughter has *Trisomy 18.*"

My heart sank. Trisomy 18, or Edwards syndrome, is a lethal abnormality. It presents as a constellation of defects, including malformations of the central nervous system, brain, heart, fingers, feet, and bowel.[2] More than fifty percent of Trisomy 18 babies are born with some type of congenital heart defect. Bill already knew that such children usually die before their first birthday and are profoundly impaired neurologically. They rarely progress in development beyond the two or three month level. He knew that the medical literature recommended comfort care only.

"Bill, I am so sorry to hear that. How is Grace dealing with this information?"

"She and her husband are devastated. And they have lots of questions. They want to be as prepared as possible under the circumstances. Do you think you could you meet with them? They may want to bring other family members as well. I hope that's okay."

"Of course, Bill. Just call Ruthie, my practice manager. I'd set it up myself, but I don't have access to my hospital calendar at home. She can take care of it first thing in the morning. Tell her we'll need forty-five minutes to an hour."

Less than one week later, Grace, her husband Buddy, Buddy's parents, Grace's mother Angie (Bill's first wife), Grace's stepmother Stella (Bill's current wife), and a maternal aunt showed up in my office. I was surprised that Bill was not there. The family told me he had to work, but I suspected that he stayed away because he already knew too much about Trisomy 18.

The eight of us gathered around the large table in our office conference room, situated well away from the babies in the NICU in the building next door. I introduced myself, gave my professional qualifications, and as a friendly opening foray I explained my long-standing professional relationship with Bill.

"I'm sorry to have to meet you under such stressful circumstances. I'm here to help you understand the situation." I paused. "Have you decided on a name for your little girl?" I have this issue about not calling fetuses and newly born sick babies "your baby," "your daughter," "your son," or "it." I like to call them by their real names. The name helps me to remember if the fetus/baby is a boy or girl and makes the conversation less impersonal. It's also a self-induced ploy to help me think of a real person, not the preemie in the corner isolette in room two. (An adult equivalent of this impersonality would be, "the diverticulitis in room 405.")

"Taylor Marie."

"That's a very pretty name. May I refer to her as Taylor?"

"Yes, that's fine."

"So, tell me what you understand about Taylor's condition."

When I'm not the first one to give a family bad news, I like to get a handle on what preconceived notions of their child's illness the family has formed. Every health care professional has his or her own manner and style of conveying bad news. Some are more compassionate; others are very blunt, even detached. Some of my colleagues routinely sugarcoat bad news to the point of bordering on deception. They tell parents what they want to hear, rather than what they need to know. Others of my colleagues remove all hope from the outset. We call that "hanging the crêpe" in Med-speak.

Explanations can be clear or confusing to parents. Frankly, some doctors are better at them than others. Some are more equipped to explain medical issues in laymen's terms. Individuals receiving bad news also differ in their intellectual and emotional capacity to take in and digest what's being said. Frequently parents will subconsciously stop listening after the first bad word they hear, like "death" or "critical" or "mental retardation." They may misinterpret the physician's words, or bend their words to be more encouraging. Parents hear what they want to hear. The H family had already met with multiple professionals: their own obstetrician, the perinatologist, a genetic counselor, and the pediatric cardiologist. I hoped that all of them had presented similar information so that the message would be clear: "We are sorry, but there is nothing we can

161

do to cure Taylor, and little to be done that will add pleasure to whatever time she has on this earth. Beyond palliative comfort care we can offer nothing more than the opportunity for you to love her. Above all, as the Hippocratic oath states: *primum non nocere*, "first do no harm." Let us not add to her suffering.

I expected to clarify the details of exactly what the H's could expect once Taylor was born. I was ready to repeat as many times as needed the "I'm sorry there is nothing more we can do" refrain. Pediatric textbooks all agree that once the diagnosis of Trisomy 18 has been established, extraordinary means for prolonging of life should not be seriously considered. I hoped that the H's had not selectively searched the Internet seeking information-of-hope, or latched on to a support group with unrealistic expectations. Many Trisomy 18 websites plant false hope and set forth impossible developmental goals for affected children. Differing attitudes toward outcome expectations often set up adversarial relationships between the parents and the doctors, nurses, and therapists who have to help the affected children and families through the saddest of times. The medical world feels that holding out the example of one in one thousand children (probably a mosaic or partial Trisomy 18) who *may* take a few steps at the age of eight or older as an example of what miracles can happen is unrealistic and cruel.

Grace seemed to be the family spokesperson. Petite, very pretty, and very pregnant; she and her handsome police officer husband made a charming young couple. She told me that she understood, from what the doctors had already told them, that Taylor had Trisomy 18 and a complex heart defect that the cardiologist said would not affect her health immediately at birth.

"We know her heart problem is serious and may cause her death eventually. She may have other abnormalities that haven't shown up on the ultrasound, like a cleft palate or intestinal obstruction. She will probably die by her first birthday." Grace's voice faded and her deep brown eyes welled up with tears. "Maybe sooner."

I waited for Grace to continue.

"Dr. Sacks, we just want to take her home with us. We know there is nothing that will make her better. We don't want any treatment that will cause her pain or more suffering. We just want to love her at home and be there with her when she dies."

I nodded. They had a good basic understanding of the situation. So far we were on the same page. Then Grace dropped the bombshell.

"The C-section is scheduled for June 25th. Can you be there?"

I was totally shocked. C-section? Whatever for? Taylor had a lethal anomaly. A C-section would be of no ultimate benefit for her and would place an additional burden on Grace's health.

"Why a C-section?" I tried to be gentle. I hoped my facial expression didn't give away my shock. Perhaps Grace had had previous uterine surgery. In that case it would have made sense not to risk uterine rupture with a vaginal birth after uterine surgery. I was sure the H family anticipated future pregnancies.

"Taylor is feet first and my obstetrician said a C-section is indicated, because if she comes out feet first vaginally her head could get stuck and she might be stillborn."

My rational (some might say too rational) mind still didn't perceive the problem. Although cesarian section is one of the safest surgeries performed today, it is not a procedure to be taken lightly. It puts a mother's health at stake to a greater degree than a vaginal delivery. Although multiple cesarian sections can be safely performed (Ethel Kennedy reputedly had eleven) and rarely limit the number of desired babies a couple can have, the procedure is definitely major surgery, and can sometimes jeopardize a mother's reproductive future.[3] And in-hospital recovery from a C-section is longer, forty-eight to ninety-six hours, compared to twenty-four to forty-eight hours for a vaginal delivery. Cost is at least twice as high. Post-delivery recovery time is also increased from two weeks to two months. A C-section delivery carries three times the complication risk of a vaginal delivery, and increases the risk of placental problems with the next pregnancy.

Natural instinct leads mothers to take any risk to benefit an unborn child. Common sense suggests that the increased maternal risk should also better the baby's chances of intact survival. But what if the risk to the mother is of no benefit to the baby? What if the infant will die regardless of the mode of delivery? Then why risk the mother's health? Yes, the breech position of Grace's infant meant a vaginal delivery was dangerous for her baby, but her baby would die anyway, so the C-section would be of no ultimate benefit to the child. Medically, I couldn't see an advantage for Taylor.

"Dr. Sacks, I hope you can understand where we are coming from. We know Taylor will die, but we just want to hold her while she's alive, even if she dies soon after birth. It may be hard for you to understand, but it's very important to us." They were partially correct. I accepted their right to hold their baby while she was still alive.

Several years back, I'd had a misunderstanding with an obstetrician over an alleged request for full heroic support for a yet unborn *anencephalic* baby.[4] He said that the parents had expressed to him their insistence on a cesarian section if their anencephalic fetus got into trouble during labor. The obstetrician said that the parents were requesting that *everything* be done to save their child, including placing the baby on a ventilator. That request for a baby with anencephaly is neither medically nor morally appropriate. I told my obstetrical colleague in no uncertain terms (actually I think I shouted in righteous indignation on the phone) that I couldn't honor their request, nor would any of my fellow neonatologists. I asked that the parents be counseled about this by one of our group of neonatologists well before the due date so they'd have no misconceptions as to the extent of care that their child would receive and our reasons for such a decision.

Actually, that obstetrician had been incorrect. During the counseling session the neonatologist uncovered that the parents had no desire for their anencephalic child to be placed on full life support. They simply wanted their seventh child to be born alive so that she could be baptized into their Catholic faith, hence their request to intervene for fetal behalf during labor. As a result of that rational request, we supplied a neonatologist at the delivery and their church provided a priest. The baby was born by vaginal delivery and was baptized immediately after birth, which helped the parents accept the fact that their daughter lived for only two hours.

Grace's cesarian section was planned for June 25. I would be off that morning, having worked the night before, but I agreed to stay a few hours more so I could attend the C-section at 10 A.M. The delivery details out of the way, or so I thought, I explained that because of the lethal nature of Trisomy 18 we did not recommend heroic measures for care even in the delivery room. I prayed that the great compassion, which I truly felt, would be obvious to the family. I didn't want to be perceived as too clinical, too utilitarian, or even uncaring, as a medical presence can sometimes convey.

"We agree with a general Do Not Resuscitate order, but we want to hold Taylor while she's alive, even if she dies in our arms in the operating room. So we'd like her to be resuscitated in the OR if that becomes necessary." This pleading statement couldn't have been more sad.

The fact is that Trisomy 18 is one of only three conditions for which the American Academy of Pediatrics specifically recommends withholding resuscitative measures in the delivery room. I wondered how to handle the situation. A repeat of the horrors of a past prolonged and painful hospital sojourn for a baby with Trisomy 18 was not a situation I wanted these young parents or their baby to experience, nor was it one I wished the staff to relive. However, there was little time to think about my response. The family expected an answer. An affirmative answer.

"If Taylor needs resuscitation, would it be acceptable to you to limit it to ventilation with a bag and mask? That would mean *not* to place a tube in her windpipe and hook her up to a ventilator. Not to give heart-stimulating drugs." As a cop and first responder, Buddy was familiar with the terms bag and mask, and tubes in the trachea.

"I'm concerned about causing Taylor pain by doing cardiac massage or placing the tube in her windpipe. If she doesn't start breathing on her own, we may be left with the decision to actively remove the tube and stop the ventilator. I'd rather you not have to face a decision like that."

I couldn't believe I was endorsing active, although limited, resuscitation for a child with a lethal condition. I was condoning actions in direct contradiction to my professional society's recommendations. But given the circumstances, the H's request seemed logical and reasonable. Hopefully, Taylor would not need more than a brief period of positive pressure ventilation. It would be terrible if their request became the start of a slide down that slippery slope of escalating care ending with heroic efforts that would only prolong Taylor's suffering.

The H's agreed with the plan of limited intervention.

"We can let Taylor stay in the OR and recovery room with you to maximize your time with her," I said.

When I offered this last variation of care, I didn't realize that it would take special arrangements to accomplish this goal. The nurses on labor and delivery were not used to providing ongoing care for any neonatal conditions other than perfectly normal term and near-term infants. And once Taylor and Grace were transferred to our mother-baby unit we would face the same issues. Mother-baby nurses care for normal babies and their mothers. Caring for a child who would feed poorly, have apnea, maybe even die in her mother's room is not in the repertoire of tasks with which mother-baby staff have any level of comfort and security. Keeping the baby in the NICU hooked up to monitors, separated from her parents was not what Grace and Buddy wanted. And NICU admission and treatment would be of no benefit to the infant. Unconditional parental love and comfort care were all the health care team could offer.

"Would you like us to have Dr. Anderson, the cardiologist who did the ultrasound on Taylor in utero, officially consult? We can do an *echocardiogram* to confirm the cardiac lesion, and he can tell you exactly what to expect once we know for sure the extent of Taylor's malformation. Given that with Trisomy 18 no surgery is indicated, there may be medications that can help if she has symptoms like breathing too fast. DORV is a tough diagnosis to make in utero, so perhaps we should confirm it."

"All right."

"There's another issue that may prove an obstacle to Taylor's care and discharge home. Babies with Trisomy 18 may be very weak and have poor suck reflexes, or they may lack coordination of suck-and-swallow. She may not be able to eat."

"So how will I feed Taylor? I wanted to breast feed."

I sighed audibly. "We have three approaches. We can allow Taylor to feed by breast or bottle when she shows us she's hungry. If she doesn't feed well, eventually she will die of dehydration or malnutrition or chemical imbalance. If Taylor cannot feed well enough, a second choice would be tube feedings. We'd place a narrow flexible plastic tube through her nose into her stomach and put the formula or expressed breast milk down the tube. It's how we normally feed premature infants. The tube can remain in place for up to two weeks before it has to be replaced. Tube feeding is usually not a long-term solution, but can be used temporarily, even at home. A third choice would only come up if Taylor gets tube feedings, doesn't look as if she will ever take enough fluid by mouth, and you want a long-term solution. The surgeons can place a *gastrostomy—a G-tube—* into her stomach through a small abdominal incision. It's permanent as long as there is a need for the tube feedings. The procedure, however, does require general anesthesia."

Some doctors might consider a G-tube a heroic measure. That would have been my thinking five years before Taylor's birth. But by the time of this conference with Taylor's family, I'd begun to think of a G-tube as a comfort measure for both patient and family. It hurts to be hungry, and as long as the feedings are absorbed, the G-tube can be a means to satisfy the baby's hunger and the parents' agony watching a child starve to death or die of dehydration because he or she cannot feed.

"But that isn't a decision you need to make now," I continued. "Even if Taylor needs tube feedings, she could be discharged on them and you can make a decision later regarding surgery for a G-tube once you see how her general health is progressing."

I was beginning to think I was giving too much information, or raising too much hope that Taylor would survive long enough to go home. "I'm sorry we cannot change Taylor's basic problem. Given the situation, all that we can do is to make you and Taylor as comfortable as possible."

Switching gears, I asked, "Have you chosen a pediatrician?" I hoped they'd picked one of the right ones, a pediatrician who would work with them and not worry about possible medical or legal aspects of allowing a baby to die a natural death at home. I hoped they'd chosen one who was personable and easy to talk with as well as knowledgeable. There aren't too many Marcus Welby's around today.

"Yes, we plan on using Dr. Munchnik, but when we spoke to him two months ago, we didn't know that Taylor has Trisomy 18."

"I'll call him and let him know. I'm sure it will be all right with him to take her on as a patient." Thank God they'd chosen wisely. Joshua Munchnick was our rising star pediatrician. He was a smart, young, compassionate, and personable physician who was not afraid or embarrassed to seek advice from others. I knew Josh would welcome the opportunity to have a new experience and would provide kindhearted care to the child and her family. They'd made an excellent choice

Love Will Have to Be Enough

Three weeks later, dressed in my green scrubs, I found myself waiting for the anesthesiologist to start Grace's spinal anesthesia. The entire extended family, most of whom I'd already met, lined the hallway outside of labor and delivery's OR. As if awaiting the birth of a normal baby, Dad was there with a camera. A professional photographer, Alexis Janeway, was also present. Alexis is one of a small cadre of wonderful professional photographers who belong to an organization called Now I Lay Me Down to Sleep. This nonprofit foundation provides a photographer on request to take photos of dead and dying babies and children with their families. Far from being morbid remembrances, these end-of-life images help parents achieve peace and closure after the death of their baby. The artistic photos foster a sense of pride in and connection to the short lives of their children. Alexis had our permission to snap any and all photographs she thought best, including Taylor Marie's resuscitation, should there be one.

A peaceful resignation filled the OR air. It was obvious that the H family loved this child despite her predicted severe handicaps and shortened life span. They were prepared to welcome her into their clan, as they would any baby. I wasn't sure I could do the same. I respected and envied them their peace of mind, open attitude, compassion, and composure.

The obstetrician made the uterine incision, and one minute later the obstetrician handed Taylor to me, into the waiting sterile blanket. The moment of truth had arrived.

Taylor did not cry. She did not even whimper.

A quick glance confirmed that she had all the features of a classic Trisomy 18. I took the first three steps of all delivery room resuscitations: I dried her off, stimulated her, and cleared her airway. Ninety percent of preterm infants, and ninety-nine percent of term infants delivered by elective cesarian section respond to these maneuvers by breathing and/or crying.

Taylor remained still and blue; she did not attempt to take a breath.

I kept my promise to Grace and Buddy. I grabbed the anesthesia bag, which was already hooked up to one hundred percent oxygen. Carefully I placed the mask over the lower half of Taylor's face and began to *bag* her at forty breaths per minute with a pressure of twenty-two centimeters of water. Her chest moved easily with each breath and her color rapidly turned pink. Her heart rate was fine. After sixty seconds of the bag-and-mask routine, she inhaled once, and then again, and then she had a sustained respiratory effort. She even treated the OR crowd to a weak cry.

I did not know then, as I do now, that for Grace and Buddy this cry was the sound of *mission accomplished*. Once they'd found out that Taylor had Trisomy 18 they'd lived in constant fear that she would be stillborn. They were terrified that they might never have a chance to hold their firstborn in life. But Taylor made it through the pregnancy and birth process. Whatever happened subsequently to Taylor would be met with sad resignation. The reward for the family was that Taylor had been born alive. I stopped the bag-and-mask ventilation and provided free-flowing oxygen for another few minutes. Then I wrapped a very pink Taylor snugly in a blanket and handed her off to a grinning Dad.

For the time being, my job was done. I was aware that the extended family was waiting in the hall. I would have to face them. I did that and explained the mini-resuscitation that had gone on, that Taylor was now stable, and that Grace was also doing well. After wishing them luck, I headed for the on-call room to pick up my overnight bag and go home, thankful for the respite from the emotion-laden situation. The rest of my neonatal colleagues had been briefed as to the care plan. Taylor would be in good hands.

Unbeknownst to me, elaborate plans had been made to accommodate Grace and Taylor as if this had been a normal, everyday situation. A friend of the H's with previous experience in newborn nursery was a nurse on labor and delivery. She volunteered to care for the mother-baby dyad in a room in L and D normally reserved for complex prenatal and antepartum cases. The goal was to keep the family together and to provide comfort care for Taylor. The baby was placed on the NICU census, leaving the family free to send the infant back to the NICU whenever they wanted, which they didn't, except to have an echocardiogram performed. The echocardiogram showed a less severe form of heart problem than DORV. Taylor had *tetrology of Fallot*. The baby would not go into heart failure, but she would turn blue. No surgeon would ever operate on Taylor because of her Trisomy 18 status and grim overall prognosis. Actually that was not a totally true statement. A previous family with a premature child with Trisomy 18 and an identical heart defect had claimed to have found a surgeon who would operate on their son's complex heart disease, but he died before he was large enough and stable enough to undergo surgery. I saw no need to convey this information to Grace and Buddy. Given Bill's medical knowledge, they probably had already thought about seeking surgical repair of Taylor's heart defect and dismissed the idea as unrealistic.

On her first day of life, Taylor experienced multiple episodes of apnea, typical for an infant with Trisomy 18. She stopped breathing for a minute or two, turned deep blue, then gasped as she recovered. Her nurse stimulated her during the very first spell. Buddy and Grace requested that Taylor not be stimulated after that one severe spell. Taylor's death spells continued for several hours. Then the apneic episodes mysteriously stopped until the day before discharge home. The family spent the four days of hospitalization talking to Taylor, praying for her comfort. They gave her permission to die. They told her she could go home to God where she would have no pain. Nearly forty friends and family crowded into the small hospital room for a dedication ceremony, a normal occurrence within the H's Baptist church. Formal baptism was postponed until the teenage years when the adolescent could make his/her own decision regarding belief. The dedication ceremony was doubly important; family and friends knew that Taylor would not live to be a teenager and would never have the competence to make any decisions.

As we anticipated, Taylor was a poor feeder at both the bottle and breast. The family declined tube feedings. They decided against gastrostomy tube placement. Grace and Buddy simply wanted to keep Taylor comfortable. As they were preparing to take her home, the apneic spells started again. They summoned me to their hospital room. "Dr. Sacks, there is one more thing we'd like to request. We'd like an apnea monitor for Taylor at home. She's started having apnea spells again. She could die during one."

Yes, she could. But we had agreed on a DNR order, so why the monitor, I wondered. "Apnea is part of Taylor's illness," I explained. "What will you do if Taylor stops breathing at home? Will you take her to the emergency room? They might put a tube in her throat and place her on a ventilator, and you said that you didn't want that, didn't you?" I was pretty defensive. I was aware of how shrill I may have sounded to them. I didn't like my tone, but I couldn't help my impatience with what I'd assumed was a closed issue. An internal struggle over control of my responses was going on between my brain and my heart. To my way of thinking an apnea monitor was an heroic—and therefore contraindicated—measure. Grace and Buddy could keep resuscitating Taylor for a long time. The apnea was a primary part of the constellation of Trisomy 18 defects, not a secondary condition to an illness that would respond to specific treatment. Repeated stimulation or mouth-to-mouth resuscitation or bag-and-mask ventilation would be cruel to Taylor and an emotional roller coaster for her parents.

"Dr. Sacks, you don't understand. We won't stimulate her if she stops breathing. That's not our intention at all. We don't want her to suffer needlessly on a ventilator in the hospital. But we don't want her to die all alone, either. We couldn't bear that. We want to be there for her when she dies. We need to be there for her sake and for ours. Without a monitor, I don't think we will get any rest. She could slip away quietly in her sleep, and we wouldn't be there. We need to be with her at the end. An apnea monitor will let us do that, and remove a lot of worry from us." Grace was quite eloquent.

The H's had obviously thought this all out. I couldn't argue with their logic. *It was not what I would have done,* I thought, but I said, "I think that's acceptable management, and a novel adaptive use of the monitor."

In one of the inexplicable ironies of life—like the cardiologist's child with congenital heart disease—granddad Bill watched as one of his former employer's current respiratory therapists explained to his daughter and son-in-law the intricacies of monitor use.

Taylor lived for thirty-three days. Grace kept a diary detailing the family's interactions with her. Every seven days her family celebrated her "week birthday," complete with Tinkerbell party hats. On her thirty-third day of life, after repeated episodes of apnea all morning, in the late afternoon Taylor died in her parents' warm and loving embrace.

Eight months after Taylor's passing, Grace and Buddy attended our annual Walk to Remember, the ceremony of commemoration our department holds to recall and celebrate the lives of children lost through miscarriage and early death. Grace was very brave; she volunteered to begin the segment of sharing stories and memories. She read a portion of a tribute to Taylor Marie, which she subsequently posted on the Trisomy 18 Foundation website. The words were and are moving and very beautiful. There were tears in the eyes of many in attendance, including mine.

Two years after Taylor Marie's passing, her baby brother was born by repeat cesarian section. He had forty-six beautiful chromosomes and cried lustily at delivery. Today he's a healthy little boy.

1. www.emedicine.com/ped/topic2509.htm
2. K. L. Jones, ed., *Smith's Recognizable Patterns of Human Malformation,* 5th ed. (Philadelphia: W. B. Saunders Co., 1997).
3. There is a small but definite risk of uterine rupture (one in three hundred in some studies) at the uterine incision site during labor in a vaginal birth after C-section (VBAC), resulting in injury or death to the baby and possible emergency hysterectomy for the mother. The American College of Obstetrics and Gynecology recommends that a trial of VBAC be undertaken only if both obstetrician and anesthesiologist are on site during the

labor (see the ACOG Practice Bulletin, "Vaginal Birth After Previous Cesarean Delivery. Clinical Management Guidelines for Obstetrician-gynecologists," American College of Obstetricians and Gynecologists, *International Journal of Gynaecological Obstetrics* 66, no. 2 (1999): 197–204). With the increased medical and legal risks of VBAC's, many institutions have stopped offering them at all. So "once a cesarian section, always a cesarian section" is pretty much a dictum. For every ten thousand women undergoing cesarian section, one to two will die, although it is hard to sort out whether these deaths are direct complications of cesarian sections (bleeding, infection, pulmonary embolism) or a result of the underlying pathology leading to the operation (see A. M. Minino, M. P. Heron, S. I. Murphy, and K. D. Koshanek, "Deaths: Final Data for 2004," *National Vital Statistics Report* 55, no. 19 [2007]: 1–120.)

4. Anencephaly is the condition of having developed no brain above the brainstem, and usually no bone or skin cove. It is uniformly lethal.

11

ROOMING IN TO DIE

Prenatal Consult

There are myriad conditions that will prompt the call for a prenatal consult. The most common reason is anticipated premature birth (secondary to spontaneous premature labor), twins or higher multiples, or rupture of the membranes well before term. At other times the premature birth is expected due to a maternal condition, such as worsening *preeclampsia*. Fetuses with major surgical congenital anomalies, chromosomal abnormalities, or other life-threatening conditions form another distinct group.

Sometimes there are difficult decisions to be made about the pregnancy. Based on information gleaned from our consultation, interventions (such as cesarian section for fetal welfare) may or may not be indicated. Should the obstetrician perform an operative delivery if the fetus is in trouble? Or should we write off an at-risk fetus with a minimal chance of intact survival for the sake of preserving maternal health or life? Parents are the ultimate decision makers. They can make informed decisions only if they know all of the facts: the chance of survival, the likelihood of severe developmental consequences for the infant, and the consideration of the intensity of the infant's pain and suffering during a long hospital stay and after discharge.

In the case of an abnormal infant, or an extremely premature baby on the cusp of viability, decisions need to be made in the delivery room. There is no time for discussion of pros and cons in the first few minutes of life. To delay treatment even for a few minutes can threaten the outcome. How far do the parents want me as the neonatologist to go as regarding initial resuscitation? May I use a bag and mask to ventilate? If that is not successful, should I cease and desist and switch to comfort care? Or should I place a tube into the baby's throat if necessary? If the infant's heart rate is absent or very low, should the team use cardiac massage? Can we perform a full *code,* including medications to jump start the heart?

In less extreme situations, such as for a routine preemie, or for a malformation that ordinarily can be treated successfully, the prenatal consultation lets the parents know what to expect immediately after birth. We try to give them a crash course in delivery room measures. We educate them about the first week of life, including topics such as lung disease, *surfactant, patent ductus arteriosus, intraventricular hemorrhage,* infection, and anticipated surgical repair in the case of a congenital abnormality. Some of us use the opportunity to encourage breast feeding. Breast is best, especially for preterm infants. Lying in bed with ruptured membranes or in preterm labor, mothers are better able to absorb information than immediately after birth. Truth be told, however, nothing short of training as a pediatrician or having had a previous very sick infant can prepare the family of a tiny and/or high-risk baby for the trials and tribulations of the rocky road that may be ahead of them.

I'd been asked by Sam Feldman, one of our perinatologists, to talk with Mrs. K, an educated, very likeable thirty-three-year-old woman, twenty-five weeks pregnant, and with chronic hypertension. She had been admitted to the hospital two days before. I suspected she'd be held hostage there for the duration of her pregnancy. All previous five pregnancies had self-terminated by spontaneous abortion prior to twelve weeks. Mrs. K's prenatal consult was not going to go well, because after careful reading of the chart I could find nothing upbeat about her high-risk pregnancy to relate to Mrs. K, no scraps of clinical facts to encourage her.

"Mrs. K?" Cautiously I opened the door and entered the room. "Hello. I'm Dr. Sacks, one of the neonatologists here at Pine Grove Hospital. May I come in?" I stood in the doorway. "Your obstetrician requested a prenatal consult. He asked me to stop by to talk to you about what to expect if you deliver your baby in the next week or so. Is this a convenient time to speak with you?"

"Yes, it's fine. Please come in."

I went over to the lounge chair and sat down across from the hospital bed. I felt that sitting down would suggest that I wanted to be there, or maybe at least that I didn't mind being there, and that the conversation I was about to have with Mrs. K was important to me. A doctor standing at the bedside can seem threatening. I felt that standing could also imply that I was in a hurry, and talking to the patient was an imposition on my time. I'd come to realize that body language and unspoken communication are very important.

So is reputation, deserved or undeserved. Many years ago I made rounds on the mothers of normal newborn infants at Pennsylvania Hospital in Philadelphia. I was a senior neonatology fellow. The physician to whom this task usually fell, Dr. Tim Biggs, my attending, had asked me to fill in for him on a Sunday morning. As I entered the second room of my twelve-room cycle, I noted on the hospital sheet that the baby had some jaundice and had been placed under phototherapy for treatment. At the worst, the phototherapy would delay the baby's discharge by a day or so. The condition was not life-threatening by any means. The baby was otherwise quite healthy.

I pulled a chair up to the bedside to chat with the baby's mother about the phototherapy lights and the possible delay in discharge.

She burst into tears before I could say anything!

"What's wrong, Mrs. J ? Shall I call your nurse?" Talk about overreaction to a minor problem! I hadn't even started my jaundice spiel.

"This is my first baby. Lots of my friends have had their babies here," sobbed the patient. "They told me if the doctor came into the room and sat down, it meant really bad news, like my baby might die!"

Evidently Dr. Biggs made lightning rounds on the newborn service. He would stick his head into the room and ask if the mother had any questions, which they didn't since they sensed from his demeanor that he really didn't want to be bothered. However, if Dr. Biggs actually came in and sat down, the rumor on the street, or in this case in the halls, was that he had come to tell you that your infant was sick enough to die. I had not been familiar with Dr. Biggs's modus operandi. This mother had misinterpreted my body language on account of a background framework of which I had been blissfully ignorant.

I began, "I've looked over your medical record, Mrs. K, and what I have to say to you is very discouraging."

"It's okay doctor. Go on, just tell me. I know it isn't good news. It hasn't been for weeks. You're here because I requested more information. My doctor didn't see any point to my having more information now, since it'll all be negative anyway. But before you go on, please try to understand where I'm coming from. I was so encouraged to get beyond my first trimester. This is as far as Jim and I've ever gotten in our previous five tries to have a baby. We've had five other desperate attempts. Each one ended much too early. We lost all those precious babies. Still, we have a lot of faith in the Lord. My husband and I are still hoping for a miracle."

This pregnancy was different. She perceived it as special, and not only because she had reached the latter part of the second trimester, but because of its special timing. "My due date is three days before my thirty-fourth birthday. I'm looking forward to having a wonderful birthday present." She smiled.

Unfortunately her due date was still nearly fifteen weeks away, and Mrs. K was confined to bed rest. Her only time to be out of bed was to use the bathroom facilities within her hospital room. Her fetus was suffering from severe *intrauterine growth restriction (IUGR)*. The baby should have weighed nearly two pounds as of the day we spoke, but his estimated weight by ultrasound was less than thirteen ounces. Furthermore, his growth had lagged behind for five weeks already, and he was symmetric, meaning that his estimated weight, length, and head growth had all been adversely affected to the same degree. Accompanying the baby's growth failure was a condition medically termed *oligohydramnios*, which means that a baby whose mother has that condition is barely floating in low levels of amniotic fluid, which is a common accompaniment of severe IUGR. In critical cases, such as this one was, lack of sufficient fluid can actually inhibit appropriate lung development. Amniotic fluid exerts a trophic or beneficial and necessary effect on lung growth. The fetus practices breathing in utero. Small amounts of amniotic fluid move in and out of the developing fetal lungs as the fetus breathes. However, fetal lung cells do not divide and grow properly when the amount of cushioning amniotic fluid is too low.

Women who rupture their membranes before twenty-one weeks gestation and do not abort spontaneously run the risk (in most studies over seventy percent) of having a baby with poorly developed, or *hypoplastic* lungs. These infants usually die within hours of birth because their lungs cannot support respiratory function.[1] Pulmonary hypoplasia means there is a reduced number of lung cells, as well as stunted development of the blood vessels of the lungs. The overall result is decreased blood flow to already inadequate lungs in the newly born infant. This condition can be devastating at birth, with death occurring within minutes to hours. Or it can be milder, with too few lung cells at birth, but sufficient gas exchange area to sustain life for a limited time. Further lung growth is also compromised by the fact that there are fewer lung cells to divide as the infant grows. There are additional detrimental effects to the lungs from the ventilator and oxygen, which are needed to support the partially hypoplastic lungs. Some babies may survive for a few months. However, at three to five months of life a baby with this condition may outgrow his lungs' capacity to take in oxygen and get rid of *carbon dioxide*. By that time his weight will have doubled or even tripled, and his metabolic needs will do the same. His stunted lungs will not sustain him any further.

That afternoon it was my job to prepare Mrs. K for the potential problems facing her baby. Even if her fetus were to be born alive and initially survive, supported by the advanced technology of the NICU, he might die as his body outgrew his lungs. I would try to explain that our goal would be the same as his parents', to work toward his going home. But when that goal became impossible, we would do what we could to make him as comfortable as possible in preparation for the inevitable.

Why tell Mrs. K about her fetus' likely poor outcome several weeks before his birth? Why not wait until she is ready to deliver? Or even after the delivery? The general intent of a prenatal consult is to provide basic information to parents at risk for an abnormal pregnancy outcome. We try to provide them with data about chances of survival and chances of normality. We hope that if the parents are armed with accurate information, they can be better prepared to face the difficult decisions that may be required of them.

Great Expectations

Just prior to walking into Mrs. K's room, I had reviewed her hospital chart and prenatal records. Her obstetrician had also filled me in with some details. A twenty-five-week fetus was clearly viable and had a survival rate exceeding fifty percent. Grayson (they had chosen a family name) was unlikely to survive in light of his tiny size and stunted lungs. Mrs. K made it clear to me that she was willing for everything to be done to her and for her baby if it would help Grayson's chance of survival.

"The outcome is in God's hands. I'm praying for the best," she said

I'm never sure of the proper response to these verbal declarations of faith. It's not that I'm uncomfortable with such expressions of belief in God's power over life and death. I just don't know how I'm expected to respond to parents' affirmations of faith in the Almighty. On the other hand, I feel a sense of relief when they say that a precarious situation is under Divine control. It somehow means that life, death, handicap, or whatever happens, for the good or bad, is ultimately out of the doctors' hands. I wish it were politically correct to express the partnership of God-the-Giver-of-Knowledge with the physician-His-earthly-partner without coming across as insensitive to those with only divine belief, or as proselytizing to those without any faith. For many years now I've believed that a proper response to being called to an emergency is not "Please God, don't let this baby be too sick or God forbid, die." In my scientifically trained, religiously oriented mind, the prayer with which I feel most comfortable is "Please, dear God, grant me the knowledge to know what to do and the skill to do it, so I can help the baby. Amen." I believe that what has occurred to threaten the baby's welfare is a *fait accompli*. I don't believe my prayers are going to alter what has already medically happened. My belief, rather, is that my job is to fix it, and God's job, if you will, is to continue to empower my brain and enable my hands to do so.

"I hope that Grayson's growth improves with bed rest. And I hope we will not see either of you until much later," I politely said as I left the room thirty minutes later. Truthfully, I did not expect such an implied positive outcome. I suspected that her fetus would die in utero. One morning the staff nurse would come in for a vital sign check, hook Mrs. K up to the fetal monitor, and would discover that there was no fetal heart beat. The baby would quietly expire in his mother's womb without ever having suffered through the daily routines of the NICU.

But I was wrong. Grayson was born three weeks later by urgent cesarian section, weighing just one pound two ounces. His appearance was reminiscent of ET, the extra-terrestrial: a huge normally proportioned head connected to a wasted body. After he was extracted from his mother's uterus, he was very blue and made no effort to breathe. To help expand his lungs we gave him surfactant through his *endotracheal tube* at seven minutes of life in the delivery room. Had he been born only one year earlier, he wouldn't have received surfactant until after his initial stabilization in the NICU, following a chest X ray to confirm that he had *respiratory distress syndrome* and that his endotracheal tube was in good position. Most likely this would have meant a delay of at least thirty to forty-five minutes, more likely one to one and a half hours, during which time his stiff lungs would have been pounded mercilessly by the ventilator's high settings, and he might have remained blue despite the ventilator. A nationwide collaborative quality improvement process led to this change in our practice, to provide immediate administration of surfactant in the delivery room.

The national collaborative Vermont Oxford Network (VON) began in 1990 as a means to collect data on very low birth weight (VLBW) infants weighing less than 1500 grams at birth. The initial philosophy of its founders was that a researcher obtains better data and can draw more valid conclusions from collecting fifty data points on two thousand babies than from two thousand data points on fifty babies. Since the typical high-risk nursery has fifty to two hundred VLBW infants a year, it was necessary to enlist many centers into the data collaborative. VON started with thirty-six centers and enrolled 2,961 infants in their first year. As of the time of Grayson's birth, the network had 557 centers and almost 46,000 births yearly. Our hospital joined in VON's second year, and was given a confidential identity number. We are given data both for our center and conglomerate data of all centers. Knowing our own secret identity number, we can compare ourselves to the conglomerate of other centers. We know the names of all the other centers, and they know ours, but no center is privy to any other center's confidential number and therefore confidential outcome statistics. Initially we submitted data on handwritten forms and by snail mail. Analysis of data was not available for six to nine months after the completion of the calendar year. Today all data is submitted electronically. Patients are de-identified in accordance with federal standards (HIPAA).[2] Ongoing summary data is available almost in real time via VON's password-protected website.

VON started a unique project related to surfactant administration. It was a quality improvement project formulated to determine if exposure to information about the benefits of early versus delayed surfactant administration could alter the performance of individual neonatal centers. The project results found that education matters and can induce changes in protocols and medical behaviors. As a result, centers like ours, who formed the experimental group and whose teams received information about the benefits of early intubation and surfactant administration in very small babies, began to give surfactant earlier, usually in the delivery room.[3] Grayson was the recipient of the benefits of this research.

On admission to our nursery, Grayson was cold. His core temperature registered a chilly ninety-four degrees. The operating room in which he had been born was frigid because its temperature was adjusted to suit the surgeons who had to stand under hot lights draped in gowns, heads covered, and hands in latex gloves. Babies are born wet and must be dried off thoroughly as quickly as possible. While trying to stabilize the infant, he had lost heat in the sixty-five-degree environment.

Often the health care team in the delivery room is so intent on the obvious lifesaving measures of providing oxygenation and ventilation, that the medical staff forgets about the mundane details of heat loss. Nearly fifty years ago one of the original American neonatologists, Dr. William A. Silverman, demonstrated that by simply placing tiny preterm infants in incubators at warmer temperatures than were commonly used, doctors could lower mortality by more than half. Today official neonatal resuscitation guidelines recommendations for tiny preemies include turning up the temperature in the OR to seventy-five degrees (at least until the baby is removed from the room) and the use of a portable chemically heated warming pad (similar to hand warmers for skiers). An alternative to the warming pad is to place the wet infant's body (not his head of course) into a plastic turkey-baster bag. Both these methods are quite successful, and the latter measure is certainly cost-effective.

Twelve hours after her cesarian section Mr. K transported his wife in a wheelchair to the unit for her first real look at Grayson. She later described to our social worker the overwhelming emotions of seeing her child alive. His tiny body and degree of illness had not registered at first, so powerful was the bonding process between mother and child. Mom had feared she would lose him before his first breath, but she hadn't. *Carpe diem*—seize the day—and enjoy it for all it is worth.

I suppose it is fortunate that parents in the NICU can feel bonds of love and attachment while disregarding tubes and intravenous lines. It's wonderful that they can take delight in the minute without thinking about what misfortune the future might hold. Their baby survived the birth process, and the here-and-now is all they can focus on. If they expected a healthy term infant they might begin to grieve the loss of perfection upon seeing the paraphernalia of the NICU. But the K's' expectation for a bouncing seven-pound baby had vanished months ago. They expected the worst. Grayson exceeded their expectations. He was alive. He had ten fingers and ten toes and a beating heart. For them that was miracle enough that night.

Attaching and Letting Go

Grayson proved to be critically ill. Low *platelets* placed him at risk for hemorrhaging into his brain and lungs. He received daily platelet transfusions for four days. In addition, his white blood cell count was extremely low (the medical name for this condition is *neutropenia*). That condition was probably due to an inadequate placenta, and the effect of his mother's chronic high blood pressure. We treated his neutropenia with intravenous *gamma globulin*, which we trusted would immediately build up his immunity and help ward off infection. He also received daily injections of the drug commonly administered to chemotherapy patients to promote the release of white cells from bone marrow into the circulation.

Grayson was also born with an outpouring of immature red cells from his marrow into his blood stream. Red cells carry oxygen, and the body releases them into the circulation prematurely before birth in conditions of chronic oxygen deprivation. Grayson could simply not derive sufficient nutrients from his mother's placenta, of which oxygen was the primary one. The decision to deliver him early was based on the belief that he would do better taking his chances with extreme prematurity outside the womb rather than continuing to dwell in what had become a hostile intrauterine environment.

Most infants, even those destined to have severe chronic lung disease, go through a period of rapid (although sometimes short-lived) improvement in the first few days after birth. We call this the "honeymoon period." In larger and more mature infants the honeymoon presages an ultimate full recovery. There was no honeymoon for Grayson.

Grayson exhibited only a partial response to surfactant and artificial ventilation. He never achieved low rates on the ventilator, and his oxygen requirement always remained above forty percent (the air we breathe is twenty-one percent oxygen). The tiny infant's blood pressure was dangerously low, necessitating the use of the cardiac stimulant dopamine to maintain blood flow to his vital organs. This need for cardiac drugs was not unusual; many infants initially need dopamine for a few days. Grayson, however, needed dopamine for the first twelve days of his life.

By his thirty-sixth hour, he was deathly ill with severe lung problems and continued low blood pressure. When his carbon dioxide level, normally fifty-five to sixty-five torr in an infant with lung disease, exceeded one hundred torr, we gave up on the conventional ventilator and wheeled out the high-tech oscillator. The oscillator was considered a form of rescue therapy in our unit, reserved for specific indications, such as a very high pCO_2 level. After a few days, maybe a week, most infants can be switched back to a conventional ventilator after the critical period has passed. Not Grayson. He remained on the oscillator for two weeks.

One evening during this period on the oscillator, a super crisis arose. At ten days of life, Grayson developed a condition known as PIE (pulmonary interstitial emphysema). Air was trapped in his lungs, but was not in the air exchange sacs where it belonged; it was outside the air sacs trapped in the lung tissue itself. Trapped air made Grayson's lungs stiff and therefore even harder to ventilate. We placed him on yet another special high-tech machine, the jet ventilator (HFJV), a device specifically made to treat PIE. We achieved stabilization, but there was little improvement in his overall condition. It appeared that Grayson was going to die unless we could affect some positive change. We discussed initiation of steroid treatment with his family. In order to save his life his parents agreed to risk the side effects of high blood sugar, high blood pressure, infection, poor growth, and an increased chance of *cerebral palsy.*

Steroids worked their magic as we had hoped they would, at least temporarily. The PIE melted away. A few days after steroids were stopped, Grayson was able to be weaned to continuous positive airway pressure (CPAP). This type of ventilatory support was delivered via a stiff plastic cannula placed in his nose. The cannula was connected to a blue box on wheels by less bulky tubing than ventilator tubing. CPAP was a great step forward for Grayson. Now he was unencumbered by his ventilator tubing and a tube in his throat. Mrs. K was able to *kangaroo* with her baby for the first time: she held him clothed only in a diaper and hat against the warmth of her breasts.[4] The twosome was covered with a blanket for additional warmth and modesty. Kangaroo care allows a mother or father to feel like a parent, perhaps for the first time since the birth of their ill child.

The joy was short-lived. The day after Mrs. K had enjoyed kangaroo care for the first time, Grayson had to go back on the ventilator on account of his worsening lung problems. Mrs. K realized, not for the first time, but somehow with more intensity and clarity, how fragile her son was. "I let myself develop a false sense of security. In retrospect it was unwarranted. It felt great for that one day; I was on top of the world. But I will never let myself go again like that, not ever, at least not until the day he comes home. The letdown is so painful," Mrs. K confided in Katie, our social worker. The roller coaster ride of the NICU had claimed another parental victim. Mrs. K would live daily in the dizzying cloud of small gains and large losses.

Grayson's condition became critical once again. He received a second course of steroids that worked their magic, and within three days of starting the steroids Grayson came off the ventilator, this time to a high flow, high humidity nasal cannula. Dr. Varedo, our pediatric ophthalmologist, reexamined Grayson's eyes. Beginning when Grayson was one month old, Dr. Varedo did serial biweekly exams on Grayson looking for evidence of retinopathy of prematurity. After that morning's exam he was concerned about the rapid progressive growth of abnormal vessels on Grayson's retina. "Linda, I'm troubled about Grayson's eyes. I'm afraid that if the retinopathy progresses further he will need laser surgery to prevent blindness," he said. "I'd better not wait two weeks to see him again. That may be too late. I'll put him down for reexam next week." Dr. Varedo scheduled a repeat examination for the following Friday.

The K's were upset by this new serious, although not unexpected, and not life-threatening development. Mrs. K's maternity leave was over. She had returned to work reluctantly, anxious to save all the time off she could for when her baby might be able to come home. Despite repeated setbacks, and heart-to-heart discussions of doom and gloom with multiple doctors and nurses, she and her husband Jim had not let go of that homecoming hope. That dream was all they had and they clung to it. Denial, I reminded myself, was a step in the grieving process.

Formula feedings were now well established. Grayson began to grow more rapidly, although he gained less than one-third ounce every day.

Not without reason, neonatal parents fixate on weight gain. Although most neonatal units have long since given up strict weight criteria for discharge, the truth is that most infants are not ready for discharge much earlier than just under four pounds. The closer one gets to that unofficial weight, the closer discharge appears on the horizon.

In the 1970's discharge weight at the prestigious University of Pennsylvania, where I had trained, was a minimum of five pounds. By the mid-1980's it was four and a half pounds, and since then had gotten lower at the majority of neonatal units. This earlier discharge is encouraged for obvious financial reasons by third-party payers, and for other reasons by parent support groups. Babies belong at home with their families, not in the psychologically sterile neonatal unit. Hospitals teem with infectious agents, and the sooner we can get an infant home, the better. We now realize that weight is an arbitrary parameter. Functionality is far more important than weight. Can the baby eat by bottle or nurse at the breast? Can she hold up her body temperature in an open bed with blankets and a hat? Can his medical needs be dealt with safely at home? Is the family prepared to care for a high-risk baby? Although weight is no longer a strict criterion for discharge, parents still view each precious ounce as one tiny step closer to going home. Pounds and ounces are a concrete figure they can understand. Grayson's weight gain was a source of joy and comfort to the K's, a sign of normalcy for his family.

In the dark recesses of my clinical heart, I harbored the secret fear that every ounce Grayson gained brought him ever so much closer to the possibility of outgrowing his lungs, closer to the possibility of dying. However, there was no point in my voicing this concern, as there was nothing that could be done about it. We could not stop him from growing! Grayson would continue to gain weight, but the growth of his stunted and diseased lungs might not keep up with his body's growth.

By six weeks he had doubled his birth weight. Grayson's actual due date was approaching. While his family knew he would not be coming home anytime soon, the EDC—medical jargon for expected date of confinement or the actual due date—would be a milestone in his life and theirs, one they planned to celebrate.

But it was not to be. Three days before what would have been his due date, Grayson looked very bad. He had already been placed on pure oxygen by nasal CPAP, an unusual maneuver we employed in order to avoid replacing his breathing tube and putting him back on the mechanical ventilator. The poor baby was working so hard to breathe that it was painful to watch him. Sedating Grayson was not an option as it might decrease his respiratory drive and cause him to stop breathing altogether, and then we would have to put him back on the ventilator, which we were trying to avoid.

A blood-gas revealed extreme carbon dioxide retention. It was the middle of the night. What was I to do? While there was no doubt that Grayson would die if he were not placed back on a ventilator, he might die even if he were placed back on the ventilator. A decision not to *intubate* would be final: the baby would certainly die. The decision to place him back on the ventilator would not be final: the tube and respirator could be removed. I sedated him and put a tube in his throat, and placed him back on the ventilator. I did that not so much because I thought it would save his life, but because it was a temporary fix. The ventilator respite would allow time for his family to adjust to the awful truth that Grayson, barring a miracle, would not survive much longer.

I phoned his family with the sad news of his having to be placed back on the breathing machine. They drove the fifty miles to the hospital and stayed at his bedside for the remainder of the night. Somehow he survived; perhaps he siphoned strength from their presence and support. In the quiet of the conference room, away from the bleeps and flashing lights of the NICU, I explained the situation to them.

"Grayson has end-stage lung disease. I'm sorry, but there is nothing that we can do to cure him. Steroids might help some and buy him some time. We could restart them if you wish." Another course of steroids might provide a temporary Band-Aid and give them additional time to adjust.

Mr. and Mrs. K were distraught. "Dr. Sacks, can we have some time to think about the steroids and what we think is best for Grayson?" they asked.

The scenario is familiar to any neonatologist dealing with devastating disease. The K's did not want to give up on Grayson. They had experienced his frequent downturns and crises, but they had also seen his turnarounds. He had rallied before. They loved him more than ever. They hoped that maybe the next course of steroids would be the magic bullet. They rationalized that if Grayson hadn't given up, why should they? No, Grayson could not speak for himself, but he was putting up a great fight. Whenever his condition had improved, they had interpreted his recovery as a testimony to his will to live. Moreover, he didn't look nearly as fragile and helpless as he had looked before. He was now almost three times his birth weight, and yet, in a way, it was this very growth that doomed him. Like some children outgrow their shoes or pants, he had outgrown his lungs. Department stores don't sell larger lungs, and he was far too small for an experimental lung transplant.

We continued full medical support. The family prayed for guidance as to the proper decision regarding steroids and continuing the ventilator. It was a very long night.

The following morning I ordered an *echocardiogram* to evaluate how severe the effect of Grayson's lung disease had been on his heart. The results were not good. The cardiac test showed that the high pressure in Grayson's scarred and undergrown lungs had led to the buildup of pressure on the right side of his heart.[5] Short of some kind of rapid improvement in his lungs, which was not likely to happen, his heart would also fail. Grayson was terminally ill.

Meanwhile the family decided to restart steroids for the third time, not so much because it would be a long-term solution, but in order to give them more time with Grayson. It was clear that when he came off the ventilator that he wasn't going to survive long term, perhaps not even short term, without needing to be placed back on the lifesaving machine. We had daily discussions about the terminal nature of Grayson's BPD, (bronchopulmonary dysplasia). I recalled (but didn't tell the K's) a similar patient more than fifteen years before. Maya had been an IUGR infant with stunted lungs. Even after she had had a tracheostomy placed, she was never able to come off of the ventilator. We let her family room in for a few days before she died. Maya and her ventilator were moved to an empty room down the hall from the NICU. Rooming in was a way of validating Maya's existence, of letting her mom and dad actually be parents, albeit in a hospital room rather than at home. It allowed extended family and friends to visit unencumbered by the two-visitors-at-the-bed-side restrictions and high tech atmosphere of the NICU.

"Would you like to room in with Grayson?" I asked.

"As if he was going home? Is that what you are suggesting, doctor?"

"Sort of. We can move him and his isolette and his oxygen and all his paraphernalia into a patient room out on the post-partum floor. You can stay with him twenty-four hours a day for a day or two or three. We can teach you how to do tube feedings if he's breathing too hard to suck from the bottle. The nurses are only a phone call away if there is a problem. Rooming in will maximize the time you can spend together."

They looked surprised and hopeful, as if this would be an experience they'd greatly appreciate.

"I'd also suggest that we plan not to place him back on the ventilator again." I was requesting a Do Not Resuscitate order from them without actually using those words. Quietly I waited for a response. It wasn't the one I expected.

"You think he's going to die, don't you, Dr. Sacks?"

My moment of truth. "Yes, I do."

I wanted to cry for them and with them and for myself and for Grayson and for every previous child with whose parents I had had this identical conversation. "You know we have done everything humanly possible to help him. His end-stage lung problems cannot be cured. We have no more medications or machines left that will help."

It was deadly quiet at the bedside. I waited for a response but there was none. I could not stand the silence, so I continued. "But I also think he'd rather be with both of you, than in the neonatal unit for whatever time he has left, if you are okay with that."

Tearfully looking at each other with love and sadness, the K's agreed that would be best for Grayson. I questioned them further to be sure they really felt that they could handle the possibility of his dying in their private room, their home away from home. They assured me that not only were they sure of their ability to cope with his death, they were thankful for the chance to orchestrate it in that way.

The respiratory therapists switched Grayson from uncomfortable bulky CPAP to a comfortable high-flow nasal cannula. He looked so much more at ease that way, and could interact with his parents and grandparents. His facial expressions would be obvious. Any photographs they might take would show his beautiful, delicate features unencumbered by tubes and catheters. We set up a mini-intensive care room in the hall down the corridor from the NICU. The family settled in to room in for the weekend. On the second day of rooming in, Grayson developed intermittent episodes of stridor and wheezing, forcing us to increase both the flow on the cannula and the concentration of oxygen to their maximums. Somehow, though, he maintained his blood oxygen level in a normal range as indicated by his pulse oximeter reading. We didn't know what his carbon dioxide level was because we didn't dare measure it. As his condition weakened he could no longer manage to suck from a bottle. It took all his energy just to breathe. With help from the nurses his mother satisfied his hunger with tube feedings.

Over a few short hours, in the descriptive words of a former colleague of mine, Grayson developed the *dwindles*. It was now apparent to all involved in his care that Grayson was terminal and that death would follow in hours to days. By Saturday evening his oxygen level was borderline. The nursing staff offered the K's the comfort measure (for them) of moving Grayson back into the unit so that professionals could care for him. The K's could resume the role of NICU parents, fully engaged but freed from the nitty-gritty of tending to the activities of daily living. The K's declined the offer. They were committed to staying the course. They were committed to being at Grayson's side, caring for him, comforting him as he died, in a setting that was as nonclinical as possible.

On Saturday night Grayson began to have occasional episodes of bradycardia. His heart rate dropped very low then spontaneously recovered. Over the course of her son's hospitalization Mrs. K had become very close to several of the NICU nurses. Mrs. K confided to Dinah, "It's so hard to let go of Grayson, to allow him to die. I know we have to, but we're having trouble finding the inner strength to let it happen. We love him so much. The pain of letting him go is awful. It's more than we can bear."

"It's okay," Dinah told her. "It's okay to let him go. Grayson knows you love him and wanted him so much. He's tired. He's working so hard. He needs an end to his suffering. He needs to rest."

"Grayson, I love you, honey, but it's okay to die. I love you. I love you, Grayson." Mrs. K whispered tenderly. Her husband cried softly at her side.

A few hours later, late Sunday morning, Grayson's heart rate acutely plummeted to thirty-seven. This time it didn't come up on its own. Mrs. K calmly called the NICU nurse to the room. Grayson was blue, despite the cannula at its highest rate, and pure oxygen. By the time I was summoned, Grayson's three-month struggle to overcome the odds with which he was cursed at birth was nearly over. Mr. and Mrs. K were holding and rocking him. They were crying. The elder K's, the paternal grandparents who had been part of the family constellation caring for Grayson since birth, were also present, offering emotional support to their son and daughter-in-law with their words and hugs and tears.

This is an awkward time for a doctor. It is a beautiful family tableau, which in the old days used to be enacted at home. Loving, grieving parents, saying good-bye to their child in a natural setting. Doctoring skills aren't needed. We health care professionals are the intruders. We don't belong in this scene. Our professional role is to listen for a heart beat and pronounce the infant dead when we cease to hear one. What caring individual wants to put a cold stethoscope to the chest of a tiny infant, waiting and hoping to hear nothing? Who wants to be in the position of hearing a slowing heart rate and having to say "not yet"? It just seems so cruel. So I waited a good ten minutes, talking to the K's, reassuring them their baby was not in pain (of this I was sure), and that he knew—of this I was not sure, how could I be? but it was a nice thought I'd like to believe—that they loved him, and that he sensed their loving embrace as he was dying. I told them they had done everything a parent could do to help their baby.

I listened at last. I heard no faint heart beat. Nothing.

"Grayson's gone. I'm sorry." More tears fell, theirs and mine: tears of sadness, heartbreak, failure, relief.

For the next four and a half hours in the sacred privacy of their room, of Grayson's first and final bedroom, the family held their baby, first one parent then the other, then the grandparents. They cried, they told stories about his short life, about the hopes they had held for him. They took their last pictures of their precious firstborn.

The funeral was held several days later in the neighboring community where the K's lived. Grayson had never set foot outside the hospital. His parents were neither rich nor famous. But there were over three hundred people at his funeral, including several nurses, respiratory therapists, and two neonatologists. I hugged his parents and grandparents. Despite his suffering and his ultimate death, the K's were grateful for the time they had with Grayson. They knew they had made the right decision not to pursue the ventilator again.

Three years later Amanda K entered the world by repeat cesarian section, weighing six pounds at full term, crying lustily. After forty-eight hours in the normal nursery she was discharged from the hospital in excellent condition with her mother. Someday her parents will tell her about her older brother, Grayson.

1. Pulmonary hypoplasia must be differentiated from immature lungs, as commonly seen in premature infants. With immature lungs, the numbers and size of cells are appropriate, but the cells' function is temporarily inadequate because of immaturity. Artificial surfactant helps tide these babies over until their own lung cells can kick in with production of surfactant within a few days of birth. With pulmonary hypoplasia, regardless of gestational age, the lungs have not developed properly for air exchange to take place.

2. Deidentification means that prior to submitting data we must remove any specific information that might allow someone to identify the specific patient. Information, such as name, date of birth, and hospital number, are removed.

3. J. D. Horbar, J. H. Carpenter, J. Buzas, et al., "Collaborative Quality Improvement to Promote Evidence Based Surfactant for Preterm Infants:

A Cluster Randomized Trial," *British Medical Journal,* 329, no. 7473 (Oct. 30, 2004), 1004.

4. Kangaroo care was developed in Bogota, Columbia, as a means to keep small babies warm and increase their survival in the absence of sophisticated incubators. In the United States we use kangaroo care to enhance bonding and stimulate breast milk production.

5. The right ventricle, the chamber that pumps blood into the lungs, is dangerously enlarged, and its wall, thickened. This condition is called *cor pulmonale*, and represents a form of heart failure, usually secondary to severe lung disease.

Glossary

Acidosis. An increased level of acid in the blood, denoting an increased hydrogen ion concentration. Acidosis can be attributed to dissolved acids, such as lactic acids, or to increased levels of carbon dioxide.

Adrenaline. Also called Epinephrine, this hormone produced by the adrenal glands increases heart rate and strength of heart contractions. It is the substance that makes our hearts race when we are frightened or under stress. During cardiac arrest adrenaline can be injected into the blood stream to restart the heart or to increase a very low heart rate.

Alveoli (singular: Alveolus). The smallest divisions of the bronchial tree, the sites where oxygen is absorbed from the air into the blood stream and carbon dioxide released into the airway during exhalation.

Ambu Bag. There are two kinds of this resuscitation device for forcing oxygen and/or air into the lungs. One is self-inflating and will work with or without an oxygen source. The other, called an Anesthesia Bag, requires a source of compressed air or medical gas to inflate. NICU's commonly use both types of devices.

Anencephaly. The condition of having developed no brain above the brainstem, and usually no bone or skin covering. Anencephaly is a lethal anomaly, commonly diagnosed by ultrasound taken early in gestation. Anencephaly and spina bifida are part of the same malformation sequence. Enrichment of food with folic acid and folic acid supplementation prior to becoming pregnant has reduced the incidence of anencephaly and spina bifida.

ANESTHESIA BAG. *See* AMBU BAG.

APGAR SCORE. The score (ranging from 0 to 10) is assigned to a newborn infant at one and five minutes of life as a quick and consistent way to convey from one medical professional to another the condition of the infant. The baby is awarded 1 to 2 points each for heart rate, color, breathing, reflex activity, and tone. The higher the score, the better the condition of the infant. The original article describing this scoring system was published in 1952 by L. Stanley James, a pediatrician, and Virginia Apgar, an anesthesiologist. It became known as the Apgar score because Dr. James was a gentleman and let Dr. Apgar have the credit!

APNEA. Greek for "no breathing," commonly used to refer to the phenomenon of preterm infants forgetting to breathe and requiring stimulation to resume normal breathing patterns. Technically, neonatal apnea is cessation of breathing for 20 seconds or longer, or a shorter period if accompanied by BRADYCARDIA or CYANOSIS.

BETAMETHASONE. A steroid hormone given prenatally to women at risk for delivering prematurely. Betamethasone works to enhance lung maturity by inducing surfactant production. It is most effective between twenty-four and thirty-four weeks gestation and works better in female rather than in male fetuses.

BPD. *See* BRONCOPULMONARY DYSPLASIA.

BRADYCARDIA. Low heart rate, usually less than eighty in a neonate.

BRONCOPULMONARY DYSPLASIA (BPD). This acquired lung disease in babies results from a combination of prematurity, insufficient antioxidant protection, exposure to oxygen, respirators, pulmonary infection, and inflammation. It is detected by changes on chest

X rays varying from general haziness to cystic appearance of the lungs. BPD comprises four stages, according to the appearance of the X ray. The patient may require supplemental oxygen, aerosol treatments, inhaled or oral steroids, and/or diuretics. BPD is responsible for increased morbidity and mortality in extremely premature infants who survive beyond the first few weeks and months of life. The label cannot be applied to a preterm infant until that baby is at least thirty-six weeks post-conception—that is, a baby born at twenty-eight week gestation cannot be described as having BPD until he is eight weeks old.

CARBON DIOXIDE. A major waste product of human metabolism, carbon dioxide is carried on red cells and dissolved in plasma and eventually excreted through the lungs. *See also* pCO_2.

CEREBRAL PALSY. Also called CP, this movement disorder results from injury to the developing or neonatal brain. CP is static, that is, it is not progressive. Most commonly, the patient is spastic (stiff), more so in legs than arms. Patients with CP can also be spastic on one side of body and not the other (called *hemiplegia*). There is also a hypotonic form of CP and an athetoid CP, which consists of writhing movements, and is related to high levels of jaundice in the newborn. Often, but not always, CP is associated with a degree of mental retardation.

CODE. Cardiac arrest, usually accompanied by respiratory arrest, is uniformly announced in hospitals today as "code blue," but also used to be known as "Dr. Heart," or "arrest page." *Code* can also refer to the resuscitation efforts, as in "run the code."

COLOSTOMY. A surgically created opening of the colon onto the abdominal wall. Feces exit the body through the colostomy into a bag.

CYANOSIS. A bluish discoloration of skin and mucus membranes due to presence of more than five grams of desaturated hemoglobin. Cyanosis usually denotes insufficient oxygen in the arterial blood. Its adjectival form is *cyanotic*.

Differential Diagnosis. Consideration of all the possible causes of a presenting symptom, condition, or abnormal lab test. After formation of the list, appropriate laboratory studies, X rays, and other tests can be ordered in logical fashion to determine the actual diagnosis. It is sometimes necessary to initiate treatment for one or more of the conditions on the list even before knowing for certain the exact diagnosis because of the dire consequences of not treating immediately.

DNR. "Do not resuscitate" order, or status. When further care is deemed futile and the patient agrees, or a competent patient with a serious disease or advanced age expresses the desire not to be resuscitated in the event of a respiratory or cardiac arrest, a DNR order is placed in the chart, and the patient is referred to as having DNR status. Parents are expected to make (or decline) such decisions for their incompetent minor children.

Dopamine. A naturally occurring neurotransmitter and potent cardiac stimulating drug that increases heart rate, dopamine is given as a constant infusion.

Down Syndrome. *See* Trisomy 21.

Ductus. Also called Ductus Arteriosus. *See* Patent Ductus Arteriosus (PDA).

Echocardiogram. An ultrasound of the heart, utilized most commonly in newborns to diagnose structural heart abnormalities or PDA.

ECMO. *See* Extra-Corporeal Membrane Oxygenation.

Edwards Syndrome. *See* Trisomy 18.

Endotracheal Tube. A flexible tube inserted through mouth or nose into the trachea (windpipe) and attached to a ventilator to help a patient breathe.

Epinephrine. *See* Adrenaline.

Evidenced-based Medicine. Medical treatment decisions based on accumulation and analysis of all available data rather than on one's own personal (and therefore limited) experience or a single article in the medical literature.

EXTRA-CORPOREAL MEMBRANE OXYGENATION (ECMO). A technique used to oxygenate infants or children with severe lung disease unresponsive to conventional therapies. Essentially a lung (and sometimes a heart-lung) bypass whereby the circulation bypasses the lungs (or lungs and heart) and blood is oxygenated with a membrane oxygenator. ECMO cannot be performed on infants less than thirty-four or thirty-five weeks gestation because of the risk of cerebral bleeding, or in infants smaller than about four pounds on account of equipment-related technical difficulties.

EXTUBATE. To remove the ENDOTRACHEAL TUBE. The procedure may be elective and intentional, or the baby may pull out his own tube, called *self-extubation*.

FONTANEL. The soft spot(s) on newborn skulls. The anterior fontanel is usually larger than the posterior fontanel. The fontanels form at the junction of the bones that comprise the skull. The bones are not fused at birth to allow for growth of the underlying brain. A large or bulging fontanel suggests that there is increased pressure in the brain.

GAMMA GLOBULIN. Also known as IVIG (intravenous gamma globulin), this blood product contains a random selection of antibodies to bacteria and viruses, and may be effective in combating infection in selective neonates.

GASTROESOPHAGEAL REFLUX. Backup of stomach contents, such as acid, formula, or milk (or food in an adult) from the stomach into the esophagus. Symptoms in neonates include refusal to eat, APNEA, spitting up, turning blue, or aspiration of food into lungs.

GASTROSTOMY TUBE. A semipermanent tube placed intra-operatively into the stomach so that a child can be fed without having to eat by mouth. Also called G-TUBE.

GROUP B STREPTOCOCCUS. Commonly called GBS (technical name: STREPTOCOCCUS ALGALACTIA), this is the most common bacterial infection in newborns during the first few days of life, and is carried in the vaginal tract of thirty to forty percent of pregnant women, most of whom are asymptomatic. Current recommendations for culturing for GBS during pregnancy and treating GBS during labor have markedly decreased the incidence of neonatal GBS and mortality from GBS.

G-TUBE. *See* GASTROSTOMY TUBE.

HEMATOCRIT. The percentage of the circulating blood that is made up of red blood cells. There are norms for all ages. Normal value at birth is forty to fifty-five percent.

HFJV. *See* HIGH FREQUENCY JET VENTILATOR.

HFOV. *See* HIGH FREQUENCY OSCILLATORY VENTILATOR.

HIGH FREQUENCY JET VENTILATOR (HFJV). A special ventilator that runs at extremely high rates, usually 7 Hertz (420 times/minute). Used as a rescue mode of ventilation in newborns with PULMONARY INTERSTITIAL EMPHYSEMA or PNEUMOTHORAX.

HIGH FREQUENCY OSCILLATORY VENTILATOR (HFOV). A special ventilator that runs at extremely high rates, usually 8 to 12 Hertz (420–720 times/minute). HFOV can be used as a primary or rescue ventilator for infants with severe lung problems, especially those with CARBON DIOXIDE retention.

HIPAA. An acronym for the privacy requirements of the Health Insurance Portability and Accountability Act of 1996. The Privacy Rule standards address the use and disclosure of individuals' health information (called "protected health information") by organizations subject to the Privacy Rule (called "covered entities") as well as standards for individuals' privacy rights to understand and control how their health information is used. A major goal of the Privacy Rule is to assure that individuals' health information is properly protected while allowing the flow of health information needed to provide and promote high quality health care and to protect the public's health and well-being.

HMD. *See* HYALINE MEMBRANE DISEASE.

HOLOPROSENCEPHALY. A severe defect of the brain that develops by the fifth or sixth week of pregnancy. The embryo's forebrain fails to divide into right and left cerebral hemispheres, resulting in midline brain and facial defects. Affected individuals have severe mental retardation and limited lifespan.

HYALINE MEMBRANE DISEASE (HMD). Also known as RESPIRATORY DISTRESS SYNDROME (RDS) or SURFACTANT deficiency disease, it is resultant lung problems caused by lack of surfactant. Infants require additional oxygen and have difficulty getting rid of carbon dioxide. Untreated infants appear to have difficulty breathing and grunt loudly. Most infants affected are less than thirty-five weeks gestation, although term infants can also have RDS. Males are more frequently affected than females. HMD is the most common cause (after isolated prematurity) for admission to a neonatal intensive care unit.

HYDROCEPHALUS. Also known as "water in the brain," this is a medical condition in which there is an abnormal accumulation of cerebrospinal fluid in the ventricles or cavities of the brain. In neonates the increased pressure inside the skull causes progressive enlargement of the head. Normal brain tissue is compressed by the expanding fluid. Definite treatment usually involves a VENTRICULOPERITONEAL SHUNT, although some forms of congenital hydrocephalus can be cured with laser surgery. Most, but not all, newborns with hydrocephalus have some degree of neurological impairment and/or mental retardation.

HYGROMA. A congenital multiloculated lymphatic lesion that is classically found in the left posterior triangle of the neck. This is the most common form of lymphangioma. It contains large cyst-like cavities containing watery fluid. Microscopically cystic hygroma consists of multiple locules filled with lymph. Cystic hygromas are benign, but can be disfiguring, can require multiple surgeries to remove, and can become infected.

HYPERALIMENTATION. A clear yellow solution containing sugar, minerals, vitamins, and elemental hydrolyzed protein source that is administered intravenously to patients who cannot take full feedings via the gastrointestinal tract. In newborns additional fats are delivered in a milky-white companion solution of dissolved essential fats. Also called TPN.

HYPOTELORISM. The condition of having one's eyes too close together. Mild degrees are considered variants of normal. Severe degrees may be associated with an underlying brain defect.

IATROGENIC. Caused by medical treatment.

ILEUS. A disruption of the normal propulsive ability of the gastrointestinal tract. It can be due to systemic factors, like low potassium or blood infection, or due to an actual anatomic obstruction.

INDEX MEDICUS. A comprehensive index of medical-scientific journal articles, published since 1879. The last issue of *Index Medicus* was published in December 2004 (Volume 45). The stated reason for discontinuing the printed publication was that online resources had supplanted it. In the good old days a researcher would go to the *Index Medicus* in the medical school or hospital library, and manually search for the subject of interest. He could copy the references or possibly make a Xerox copy of the pages, and then search in the library's bound journals for the specific articles. Once found, the researcher could copy the articles for his own files. Prior to the 1960's, researchers would have to read the articles in the library and take notes! Today this system is supplanted by search engines such as PubMed. Many journal articles can be directly downloaded from the internet.

INHALED NITRIC OXIDE. *See* iNO.

iNO (INHALED NITIRIC OXIDE). NO (nitric oxide) is a naturally occurring molecule that acts as a catalyst leading to dilation of blood vessels. If mixed in tiny amounts (up to twenty parts per million) in inhaled gas, it causes dilation of the pulmonary arterial vessels and increased blood flow to the lungs. Since it is rapidly metabolized in the lungs, it has little or no effect on the systemic blood pressure. In the 1990's it was once declared "molecule of the year."

INTRAUTERINE GROWTH RESTRICTION. Growth in the fetus less than the tenth percentile. Also called IUGR.

INTRAVENOUS. In the vein, or given by vein, as opposed to into the muscle or by mouth.

INTRAVENTRICULAR HEMORRHAGE (IVH). Bleeding into the fluid-filled ventricles (spaces) in the brain, which occurs in up to 45 percent of preterm infants less than thirty weeks. Small amounts of blood, called grade 1 and grade 2 IVH, do not alter prognosis for life or development. Larger hemorrhages, called grade 3 and grade 4, can cause death in the smallest infants, and frequently lead to developmental problems and/or HYDROCEPHALUS.

INTUBATE. To place a breathing tube into the trachea or windpipe in order to suction secretions, give medications, or place the baby on a ventilator.

IUGR. *See* INTRAUTERINE GROWTH RESTRICTION.

IV. INTRAVENOUS line.

IVH. *See* INTRAVENTRICULAR HEMORRHAGE.

IVIG. *See* GAMMA GLOBULIN.

JCAHO. The Joint Commission on Accreditation of Healthcare Organizations, also called Joint Commission. This agency sets national standards for organization, governance, and patient safety in hospitals, home health agencies, surgery centers, and nursing homes, and also conducts periodic inspections to ensure compliance. Their unannounced visits strike fear in the hearts of administrators.

KANGAROO CARE. A program initially developed in Bogota, Columbia, as a means to keep small babies warm and enhance their survival in the absence of sophisticated incubators. In the United States we use kangaroo care to enhance bonding and stimulate maternal milk production. The infant, clothed only in a diaper and hat, is held skin-to-skin on the parent's exposed chest. The parent's chest and baby are covered with a blanket for warmth and modesty.

KILOGRAM. The metric measure of 1000 grams. The equivalent in avoirdupois is two pounds three onces. The metric system is used all over the world except for the United States.

KREBS CYCLE. A complex series of chemical reactions in all cells that utilize oxygen as part of their respiration process, producing waste product of CARBON DIOXIDE and preserving the energy liberated in the reaction in a compound rich in high-energy phosphate bonds, adenosine triphosphate (ATP). Hans Adolph Krebs won the Nobel Prize for Physiology or Medicine in 1953. The Krebs cycle constitutes the discovery of the major source of energy in all living organisms.

LACTIC ACID. A by-product of anaerobic metabolism.

LAMINAR FLOW HOOD. A carefully enclosed bench designed to prevent contamination of biological samples, or any particle-sensitive device. These hoods provide a constant flow of air out of the work area to prevent room air from entering. The air flowing out from the hood suspends and removes contaminants introduced into the work area by personnel. The most important part of a laminar flow hood is a high efficiency bacteria-retentive filter. Room air is taken into the unit and passed through a pre-filter to remove gross contaminants. The air is then compressed and channeled up behind and through the HEPA filter (High Efficiency Particulate Air filter) in a laminar flow fashion—that is, the purified air flows out over the entire work surface in parallel lines at a uniform velocity. The HEPA filter removes nearly all of the bacteria from the air. Complex medical fluids such as hyperalimentation are typically assembled sterilely under such hoods.

LEVEL II NURSERY. The middle-level intensive care neonatal unit. Capabilities of such units vary from region to region and state to state. Some states set guidelines for severity of illness or degree of prematurity that can be handled. The average level II unit does not care for infants less than twenty-eight weeks gestation, or for surgical patients.

LEVEL III NURSERY. The tertiary neonatal intensive care unit, which cares for premature infants of all degrees of prematurity and severity of illness. Level IIIA does not care for surgical babies, Level IIIB does. Infants requiring open-heart surgery and ECMO require Level IIIC intensive care.

MALROTATION. A congenital defect in the attachment of the bowel, allowing it to coil around on its blood supply. The twisting of blood vessels may cut off the blood supply to the area, resulting in gangrene of part or all of the bowel.

MECONIUM. Fetal stool, composed of sloughed intestinal epithelial cells, lanugo (fine baby hair), mucus, desquamated fetal skin cells, swallowed amniotic fluid, and bile.

MECONIUM ASPIRATION SYNDROME. An inflammatory and physiologic process that results from MECONIUM getting into the airways. The viscous substance plugs up smaller airways. The bile salts in meconium deactivate naturally occurring SURFACTANT. Without surfactant, air sacs collapse. Through its binding of zinc, meconium also promotes bacterial overgrowth in the lung.

META-ANALYSIS. A relatively recent statistical technique that combines the results of many different studies on hundreds of patients, performed by different investigators in separate institutions at different times, and analyzes the data as if it were one large study, thereby increasing the power to find a small difference between two therapies.

Metabolic Acidosis. Acidosis caused by accumulation of acid in the blood. Most commonly, the acid is lactic acid, produced when there is insufficient oxygen reaching the tissues.

Metabolic Screening. Every state in the United States is mandated to screen newborn infants before eight days of age for a minimum of nine inborn errors of metabolism that, left untreated, result in death or severe disability. Many of the disorders, if treated quickly enough after birth, permit normal or near-normal development. In some states testing also includes screening for blood disorders such as sickle cell anemia and thalassemia. Testing is done on mere drops of blood. This testing is sometimes referred to as "PKU" testing, as PKU (phenylketonuria) was the first disorder for which screening was available. Screening is now available on drops of blood for over sixty disorders, and the number gets larger each year.

MMHG. Millimeter of mercury (Hg is symbol for mercury) is a unit of pressure equal to 0.001316 atmosphere. Atmospheric pressure at sea level is 760 mmHg, also called a torr; named after Torricelli. Physiologic pressures, such as blood pressure and intraocular pressure, are expressed as mmHg. Gas pressures can be expressed as mmHg or torr. A systolic blood pressure of 120 mmHg means that the systolic pressure is equivalent to air pressure that will support a column of mercury 120 millimeters high in a barometer.

Nasogastric Tube. A flexible plastic tube that passes through the nose (or mouth, in which case it is called an orogastric tube) into the stomach, and is primarily used for feeding premature infants who cannot coordinate sucking, swallowing, and breathing.

NEC. *See* Necrotizing Enterocolitis.

Necrotizing Enterocolitis (NEC). An infectious and/or inflammatory condition of the bowel wall with an acute, sometimes fulminating onset, characterized by appearance of Pneumatosis Intenstinalis, air in the bowel wall. NEC is ordinarily a disease of extremely preterm infants, but term infants can develop it as well.

Throughout the last four decades multiple risk factors for NEC have been identified through retrospective studies, including cocaine, extreme prematurity, blood transfusion, and hypotension.

NEONATAL NURSE PRACTITIONER (NNP). A mid-level provider of neonatal care. Training consists of a bachelor's degree in nursing, at least a few years bedside experience in neonatal intensive care, and a master's degree as a nurse practitioner in neonatal care. NNP's are licensed to perform all aspects of diagnosis, evaluation, and treatment of both sick and well newborns under the supervision of a neonatologist.

NEONATOLOGIST. A physician who specializes in the care and treatment of newborn infants from the first minute of life until discharge from the hospital (which may be at six months of age for tiny premature infants). Current requirements for training include three years of pediatric residency followed by three years of fellowship training. The last year of fellowship typically is dedicated mostly to research, with patient care as an on-call doctor. Neonatology became a recognized subspecialty of pediatrics in 1975, and specialty boards are required every seven years.

NEUTROPENIA. A low white blood cell count, often a sign of overwhelming infection in the newborn.

NICU. An acronym for neonatal intensive care unit, a specialized unit for the care of all infants less than thirty-five weeks gestation, larger infants with medical problems, and infants with cardiac or surgical illnesses. NICU's are usually staffed with neonatologists, neonatal nurse practitioners or physician assistants, specially trained nurses, and neonatal respiratory therapists. Most large units also have their own dietician and social worker.

NNP. *See* NEONATAL NURSE PRACTITIONER.

NOSOCOMIAL. Hospital acquired, as in "nosocomial infection." It is considered a "never should happen" event. It is considered to occur when an infection is diagnosed after a patient has been in the hospital for more than three days.

OLIGOHYDRAMNIOS. A low level of amniotic fluid associated with fetuses who have no kidneys, obstructed bladders, chromosomal anomalies, or placental insufficiency. Most commonly found with fetuses that have IUGR.

ORIENTEES. Professionals of any health sciences group (nurses, respiratory therapists, et al.) who have graduated from the appropriate school and are licensed, but are new at the job. They are paired with an experienced professional (preceptor) from the same discipline for a defined period, during which they are oriented to the details of their role, and are taught the appropriate methods and skills they need to work independently. The period of orientation varies from days to weeks, depending on the area in which they work. A nursing orientee in NICN typically remains an orientee for six to twelve weeks.

OSTOMY. A surgically created opening of the bowel onto the surface of the abdomen. Used in neonatology primarily as a temporary means to bypass injured areas of bowel.

PARENTERAL NUTRITION. *See* HYPERALIMENTATION.

PATENT DUCTUS ARTERIOSUS (PDA). As a fetus, each of us has a small blood vessel (ductus arteriosus) that connects the main artery going to the body (the aorta) with the main artery going to the lungs (pulmonary artery). This extra blood vessel acts as a conduit to direct blood away from the lungs in utero. The placenta is the organ of respiration before birth, and our lungs are essentially biding their time until we are required to breathe air. The ductus normally constricts soon after birth in response to ambient oxygen, effectively closing down this conduit. In preterm infants the ductus may not respond to oxygen, and can stay open indefinitely. But the direction of blood flow changes: too much blood goes to the lung, worsening lung status. When the vessel stays open, it is called a patent ductus arteriosus or PDA.

pCO2. Partial pressure of carbon dioxide. Normal is thirty-five to forty-five. Measured in torr.

PDA. *See* PATENT DUCTUS ARTERIOSUS.

PERINATOLOGIST. Obstetrician with subspecialty training in evaluation and treatment of women with high risk pregnancies, such as threatened prematurity, high blood pressure, diabetes, or multiple gestation. Training consists of four years of OB/GYN residency, followed by three years of perinatology fellowship.

PERIVENTRICULAR LEUKOMALACIA (PVL). A softening and destruction of the white matter that surrounds the lateral ventricles of the brain, diagnosed initially by cranial ultrasound, and confirmed by MRI. Its presence correlates well with future development of cerebral palsy. It may be cystic with visible holes in the brain substance or non-cystic.

pH. The measurement of acid-base balance in the body, The normal range of pH is 7.35 to 7.45. The limits of acceptable pH for a sick preemie are 7.20 to 7.50. Because pH units are unique measurements based on logarithmic functions, the drop of just 0.2 units, from 7.40 to 7.20, represents a doubling of the acid concentration.

PHENOBARBITAL. A sedating drug commonly used to control seizures.

PHRENIC NERVE. The nerve formed by nerve roots C3-C5, it delivers motor nerve impulses to the diaphragm. Paralysis of the phrenic nerve can result from a birth injury or may rarely occur congenitally.

PIE. *See* PULMONARY INTERSTITIAL EMPHYSEMA.

PLACENTA ACCRETA. A rare condition in which the placenta grows into the wall of the uterus. After delivery it does not detach. The patient bleeds profusely and usually requires a hysterectomy to control the blood loss. It occurs much more commonly in a uterus that has undergone a previous C-section.

PLATELETS. Tiny cells derived from bone marrow that help blood to coagulate.

Pneumatosis Intestinalis. Appearing on X ray as multiple soap bubble-like areas within the wall of the intestines, these bubbles represent air trapped between the mucosal lining of the gut and the muscular layer that encircles it. Air is not a normal resident of the bowel wall. Pneumatosis intestinalis in a newborn equals Necrotizing Enterocolitis.

Pneumopericardium. A collection of air in the pericardial sac surrounding the heart. The air under pressure around the heart restricts its expansion, acting to constrict the heart's pumping action. The heart cannot fill with blood. It is usually rapidly fatal if not treated promptly.

Pneumothorax (PT). An accumulation of air inside the chest outside the lungs within the pleural space. Pneumothorax usually occurs in infants with severe lung problems who are also on ventilators, but can occur without a ventilator, or even spontaneously without lung disease. Large pneumothoraces under tension require immediate treatment and evacuation of the air which is compressing the lungs and possibly the heart.

pO_2. Partial pressure of oxygen in the blood.

Polycythemia. Too many red cells, too high a hematocrit, generally over 60 percent in the newborn. Complications of polycythemia include blood clots, pulmonary hypertension, low blood sugar, and jaundice.

Polyhydramnios. Too much amniotic fluid. Polyhydramnios may indicate a neurologically impaired fetus or a gastrointestinal obstruction; also commonly found in diabetic pregnancies.

PPHN. *See* Primary Pulmonary Hypertension of the Newborn.

Preeclampsia. A medical condition in which hypertension arises in pregnancy in association with significant amounts of protein in the urine. Preeclampsia refers to a set of symptoms rather than any causative factor, and there are many different causes for the condition. Blood pressure elevation is the most visible sign of the disease, but renal and liver failure and seizures can also occur. Preeclampsia may develop from twenty weeks gestation, is considered early onset before thirty-two weeks. Early onset disease is associated with increased fetal and maternal morbidity. Apart from cesarean section or induction of labor (and therefore delivery of the placenta), there is no known cure. It is the most common of the dangerous pregnancy complications; it may affect both the mother and the unborn child.

PRIMARY PULMONARY HYPERTENSION OF THE NEWBORN (PPHN). The failure of the normal circulatory transition that occurs after birth. It is a syndrome characterized by marked pulmonary hypertension that causes low levels of oxygen in the blood and right-to-left shunting of blood away from the lungs through the patent foramen ovale and patent ductus arteriosus. With inadequate pulmonary perfusion, neonates are at risk for developing refractory hypoxemia, respiratory distress, and acidosis.

PRIMIGRAVIDA. A woman who is pregnant for the first time.

PROSTAGLANDINS. A member of a group of lipid compounds, derived enzymatically from fatty acids and having important functions in human physiology. In neonates a prostaglandin is primarily responsible for keeping open the ductus arteriosus.

PULMONARY HYPERTENSION. *See* PRIMARY PULMONARY HYPERTENSION OF THE NEWBORN (PPHN).

PULMONARY HYPOPLASIA. A condition of too few lung cells, resulting from inadequate volumes of amniotic fluid or a space occupying lesion in the chest, thereby restricting lung development in utero.

PULMONARY INTERSTITIAL EMPHYSEMA. Air trapped in the lungs, but not in the air exchange spaces where it belongs, but located in the lung tissue itself. Trapped air makes the lung stiff and difficult to ventilate. Also called PIE, it is a not uncommon result of ventilation at high pressures in infants with severe lung disease.

Pulse Oximeter. A noninvasive device used to measure the percentage of hemoglobin saturated with oxygen. Acceptable numbers in the newborn are 85–95%.

PVL. *See* Periventricular Leukomalacia (PVL).

RDS. *See* Hyaline Membrane Disease (HMD).

Resident. A doctor in training, who has completed medical school and a first training year called an internship. Residents can be state-licensed, but are not board-eligible until completion of their entire residency of three to six years, depending on the specialty.

Respiratory Distress Syndrome (RDS). *See* Hyaline Membrane Disease (HMD).

Retinopathy of Prematurity (ROP). Abnormal tortuous development of retinal blood vessels due to a combination of too much oxygen and extreme prematurity. Formerly called retrolental fibroplasia (RLF), ROP was once the leading cause of childhood blindness in the United States.

Retrolental Fibroplasia (RLF). *See* Retinopathy of Prematurity (ROP).

ROP. *See* Retinopathy of Prematurity.

Shunt (or Ventriculoperitoneal Shunt). A device commonly used to treat Hydrocephalus, the swelling of the brain due to excess buildup of cerebrospinal fluid. Shunts can come in a variety of forms, but all of them consist of a pump or drain with one end placed in the cerebral ventricle and the other connected to a long catheter, the end of which is usually placed in the peritoneal cavity.

Spastic Quadriplegia. A developmental abnormality that results from an injury to the motor cortex of the brain. The infant develops tightness—spasticity of both arms and legs. He has trouble with gross and fine motor skills. In its mildest form, the patient is clumsy and may walk on his toes. Spastic quadriplegia can also affect speech. In its most severe form the patient develops contractures and is confined to a wheelchair. Frequently, although not always, spastic quadriplegia is associated with a degree of mental retardation.

STAPHYLOCOCCUS AUREUS (also called Staph Aureus). A bacteria that causes severe infections of the skin, blood, lungs, and spinal fluid in all age groups, specifically in the newborn. Staph Aureus is not sensitive to penicillin. The treating of staph infections requires special antibiotics. Some staph has evolved resistance even to these special antibiotics, and is called MRSA ("mersa"), methicillin resistant Staph Aureus. During the 1940's to the 1960's Staph Aureus was responsible for serious outbreaks in newborn nurseries. It is now experiencing a resurgence as a severe pathogen in NICU's.

STREPTOCOCCUS ALGALACTIA. *See* GROUP B STREPTOCOCCUS.

SUBCUTANEOUS EMPHYSEMA. Presence of gas or air in the tissue beneath the cutis of the skin. Since the air generally comes from the chest cavity, subcutaneous emphysema usually occurs on the chest, neck, and face. Subcutaneous emphysema has a characteristic crackling feel to the touch, a sensation that has been described as similar to touching Rice Krispies.

SURFACTANT. Phospholipid containing substance that lines the lungs' air sacs and prevents collapse of the individual ALVEOLI. Artificial surfactant derived from cows and pigs is available commercially to treat premature infants.

TETROLOGY OF FALLOT. Form of congenital heart disease in which there is (1) a large VSD, (2) an aorta which is displaced so that it overrides the VSD, (3) a pulmonary stenosis just below the actual pulmonary valve, and (4) thickened muscle of the right ventricle. It is one of the most common forms of congenital heart disease and is generally amenable to surgical correction.

THYROID STIMULATING HORMONE. *See* TSH.

TIDAL VOLUME. The amount of gas inhaled and exhaled in one respiratory cycle.

TORR. A unit of pressure chosen to be roughly equal to the fluid pressure exerted by a millimeter of mercury. A pressure of 1 Torr is approximately equal to 1 mmHg. Partial pressure of oxygen and carbon dioxide in the blood is measured in Torr.

TOTAL PARENTERAL NUTRITION. *See* HYPERALIMENTATION.

TPN. *See* HYPERALIMENTATION.

TRACHEOSTOMY. A surgical hole cut in the windpipe either to allow passage of a tube to bypass an obstruction in the airway or for permanent placement of a breathing tube.

TRISOMY 13. A syndrome in which infants' cells have three copies, rather than the normal two of chromosome #13. Infants display midline facial defects such as HYPOTELORISM and cleft lip and/or palate, heart defects, extra fingers, fused fingers, and APNEA. Trisomy 13 is considered lethal.

TRISOMY 18. Also known as Edwards syndrome, it is a syndrome in which infants' cells have three copies, rather than two of chromosome #18. It presents as a constellation of defects, including malformations of the central nervous system, brain, heart, fingers, feet, and bowel. More than 50 percent of Trisomy 18 babies are born with some type of congenital heart defect. These infants usually die before their first birthday and are profoundly impaired. They rarely progress in development beyond the two- or three-month level.

TRISOMY 21. A syndrome in which infants' cells have three copies, rather than two, of chromosome #21. It is also called Down syndrome after the doctor who discovered the syndrome. Infants display mongoloid faces with epicanthal eye folds, flattened nose, and downturned mouth. Fifty percent of infants with Trisomy 21 have congenital heart disease. Infants also have an increased incidence of gastrointestinal obstructions, hypothyroidism, and chance in later life of developing leukemia. Down syndrome is accompanied by a degree of mental retardation, usually mild to moderate.

TSH (THYROID STIMULATING HORMONE). The hormone released by the pituitary gland that stimulates the thyroid gland to produce thyroid hormone. Lack of sufficient thyroid hormone in the newborn causes cretinism, short stature, and nonreversible mental retardation.

VENTRICULAR SEPTAL DEFECT (VSD). A hole between the left and the right ventricles, the pumping chambers of the heart. Defect can vary in size from pinhole to massive. Small VSD's usually close on their own. Larger ones may need to undergo a surgical procedure. Infants with large defects are subject to developing congestive heart failure during the first few weeks of life. VSD is the single most common congenital heart defect.

VENTRICULOPERITONEAL SHUNT. Device used to treat hydrocephalus, the swelling of the brain due to excess buildup of cerebrospinal fluid. If left unchecked, the cerebral spinal fluid can build up leading to an increase in intracranial pressure, which can lead to further brain damage in newborns. Shunts consist of a pump or drain connected to a long catheter. The pump end is placed inside the fluid-filled ventricle of the brain, and the end of the catheter is placed in the peritoneal cavity in the abdomen. The pump contains a pressure-sensitive valve. When the preset pressure is exceeded through the build up of fluid in the brain, fluid flows through the pump down the catheter into the peritoneal cavity, where it is absorbed into the blood stream.

VLBW. Very low birth weight infants, by definition infants less than 1500 gm at birth (3 pounds, 5 ounces) regardless of gestational age. Most infants weighing less than 1500 grams are also less than thirty weeks gestation.

VP. *See* VENTRICULOPERITONEAL SHUNT.

VSD. *See* VENTRICULAR SEPTAL DEFECT.

DR. LINDA MANN SACKS, a native of Philadelphia, is a magna cum laude graduate of the University of Pennsylvania. She received her medical degree from the College of Physicians and Surgeons of Columbia University in New York City in 1973. Dr. Sacks took five years to complete her degree, taking a year off between her third and fourth year of studies to give birth to her first child, the first female student at P&S to ever do so. After internship and residency in pediatrics at the Children's Hospital of Philadelphia, she completed a fellowship in neonatal-perinatal medicine at the University of Pennsylvania.

Dr. Sacks is board certified in pediatrics and neonatal-perinatal medicine. Following a short career in academic medicine at the University of Pennsylvania, she moved to Savannah, Georgia, where she has practiced clinical neonatology since 1983. Dr. Sacks is associate clinical professor of pediatrics on the faculty at Mercer University School of Medicine. She is currently the medical director of an eight-physician, six-nurse practitioner group and oversees a neonatal intensive care unit that admits eight hundred medical and surgical patients a year. She is a past president of the medical staff at Memorial University Medical Center in Savannah.

Dr. Sacks has a reputation for common sense, frankness, and integrity: what you see is what you get. In her spare time she writes poetry, reads mysteries, and is an active community volunteer. She and her non-physician-husband, Stephen, have three grown sons, three wonderful daughters-in-law, and, so far, two grandchildren. *Valley of Tiny Shadows* is Dr. Sacks's first book.